NICK FELL

CW00951833

SMALL WONDER

the making of the nano

Philip Chacko
Christabelle Noronha
and Sujata Agrawal

Foreword by
Ravi Kant, Vice-Chairman, Tata Motors

westland

westland ltd
Venkat Towers, 165, P.H. Road, Maduravoyal , Chennai 600 095
Email: pub@westland-tata.com; phone: 044 42918501

23/181, Anand Nagar, Nehru Road, Santacruz East, Mumbai 400 055
Email: enq.mum@westland-tata.com; phone: 022 28517129/28517130

No. 38/10 (New No.5), Raghava Nagar, New Timber Yard Layout, Bangalore 560 026
Email: enq.blr@westland-tata.com; phone: 080 26742326

Survey No. A - 9, II Floor, Moula Ali Industrial Area, Moula Ali, Hyderabad 500 040
Email: enq.hyd@westland-tata.com; phone: 040 65262155/156

47, Brij Mohan Road, Daryaganj, New Delhi 110 002
Email: enq.del@westland-tata.com; phone: 011 43588213/217

Published by westland ltd 2010

Copyright © Tata Sons Limited 2010

Cover design by The Information Company

Printed at Thomson Press (India) Ltd.

10 9 8 7 6 5 4 3

ISBN 978-93-80658-59-9

Contents

Acknowledgements   I

Foreword   III

Chapter 1
The beginning   1

Chapter 2
The challenges   26

Chapter 3
The cost frontier   59

Chapter 4
From Singur to Sanand   72

Chapter 5
The first look   95

Chapter 6
The world reacts   106

Chapter 7
Nano in a nutshell   123

Chapter 8
The Tata Motors story   132

References   147

Milestones   148

Acknowledgements

The writing of this book would not have been possible without the help of a whole lot of people, especially the engineers and other professionals at Tata Motors. To begin with, we owe a huge debt to Tata Motors vice chairman Ravi Kant, whose endorsement and encouragement got us started on the road to telling the story of the Nano.

There are many more we cannot thank adequately enough for the patience and generosity they showed in meeting us, in answering our countless questions and in educating the near-illiterates that we were in all matters motoring. Girish Wagh, who headed the Nano development programme, was an enormous fount of knowledge and information. Prakash Telang, Tata Motors' managing director for India operations, C Ramakrishnan, the chief financial officer, and Debasis Ray and Arup Mukherji, both from corporate communications, went out of their way to lend us assistance.

Priyadarshan Kshirsagar, head of the manufacturing planning team, and his colleagues, Atul K. Vaidya and Jaydeep Desai, enabled us to come to grips with the nitty-gritty of the project, as did Jay Bolar and GR Nagabhushan from Tata Motors' Engineering Research Centre. Designer Nikhil Atmaram Jadhav, safety specialist Anil Kumar, RG Rajhans from body systems engineering, Sam Johnny and Vivek Sahasrabuddhey from the new product introduction team, vehicle integration head Abhay Deshpande and power train expert Sanjay Sablok provided us an inside look at the different sets of skills that contributed to the crafting of the small car.

There were others, too, who set aside time and effort to add to our understanding of how the Nano project came to fruition: Vikram Sinha of customer support and marketing maven S Krishnan; BB Parekh and Prashant Saxena of the sourcing group; head of construction MB Kulkarni; MB Paralkar from the corporate social responsibility function; Ramesh Vishwakarma from manufacturing; head of human resources for the small-car project, Dilip Sengupta; Sunirmal Patra, chief of security at Singur when the problems there unfolded; and Amarjit Singh Puri, a senior general manager with Tata Motors who was a trove of tales that could be told and some that could not.

Additionally, we are grateful to Tata Motors' dealers Arun Vartak and Amit Rathod for sharing their experience of selling the Nano, and to Ashok Vichare, Harish Dayaram Thakur and Arun Kejkar, proud owners all of the car like no other.

Our sincere thanks are also due to R Gopalakrishnan, executive director, Tata Sons, and a member of the board of directors of Tata Motors, whose support was a significant factor in the publication of this book.

Going beyond Tata Motors' organisation and those associated with it, we had the benefit of being able to count and depend on some exceptional professionals. *Small Wonder: The Making of the Nano* would have been a lesser work without the editing expertise of Kiron Kasbekar. Sujata Agrawal was a rock of support through every stage of the publication's progress. Shilpa Naresh, who designed the book, and Arushi Agrawal and Ketayun Bamji pitched in to play crucial roles.

There are, for sure, quite a few names we have missed acknowledging. For that we seek pardon, as we do for any factual errors and other inky embarrassments that may have crept into this work. The fault for those is entirely ours.

Philip Chacko
Christabelle Noronha

Foreword

The story of the Nano begins with the dream that Ratan Tata, the chairman of Tata Motors, had of providing an opportunity to millions of Indians to own a safe and affordable means of personal mobility, and thereby to improve their quality of life. The realisation of this dream is what has made the Nano such a talked about and widely praised car, an automobile with the promise and the potential to change the existing paradigm of the automotive industry not just in India but worldwide.

This innovative effort is in line with the 125-year-old tradition of the Tata organisation. The Nano is part of the continuum, a contribution by Ratan Tata to an emerging India eager to burst into the international arena.

It takes several ingredients to convert even the best of ideas into a resounding success. I will touch upon a few that have made the Nano an icon for India's emerging middle class, while generating a kind of awe across the world that transcends class, region and nationality.

Innovation is an essential plank to build the edifice of success. Millions of families riding on two wheelers in unsafe vehicles and exposed to the elements is a common sight in India. It took the imagination of one person to see the need for a safe and comfortable alternative. That's innovative thinking. The innovation solution was creating an attractively designed car that allows a family of four to travel in comfort and safety — and delivering this car at a declared price of Rs1 lakh.

We at Tata Motors held firm on the Rs1-lakh price even while the original concept of a basic rural vehicle, which we had in mind initially, evolved and morphed into a full-fledged and properly modern car that meets all safety and emission requirements. We held firm to our promised price while commodity costs and other expenses skyrocketed. Target costing, new product development processes, project management by a young team — all of these were examples of innovation, and they allowed us to overcome traditional mindsets and conventional work systems. Technological breakthroughs, and the consequent award of 32 patents to Tata Motors in relation to the Nano development programme, contributed significantly.

Discipline and focus ensured that we never took our eyes off our objective. There were many occasions when, in trying to balance contradictory requirements, our costs shot up or our performance fell short of the desired mark. This raised questions about the viability of the project and whether we should continue with it or abandon it all. But each time a setback happened, the Nano team paused, took a deep breath and recharged itself. These were not people who knew how to accept failure.

Teamwork was critical to the Nano project's success. Everyone, from the chairman to the shop-floor employee, was part of a common endeavour, and this spirit was reflected in all of the 1,000-odd people involved in the development of the small car. We understood our individual responsibilities and we willingly made accommodations and adjustments for our colleagues and compatriots so that no gaps cropped up anywhere. We shared the agonies and disappointments the project faced together, as we did when the decision to shift the plant from Singur to Sanand was taken. And we shared the ecstasies of achievement, like on January 10, 2008, when the Nano was unveiled to an admiring world at the Delhi Auto Expo.

For every member of the Nano team, working on the project was a once-in-a-lifetime opportunity, where they got the chance to interact at a personal level with Ratan Tata and observe him at close quarters. They would hang onto his every word and gesture, and they were only too eager to do what he wanted them to. It was an amazing display of team dynamics and an exceptional example of how a group of people can be motivated to reach for the stars, to reveal capabilities they may not have known they possessed.

There was a never-say-die belief that characterised the Nano's development team's approach right through the project. This enabled the team to emerge spiritedly from the depths of disappointment and despondency, from disasters anticipated and unforeseen. This spirit encouraged us to get through the Nano's dark moments, which had a habit of popping up irregularly but with uncaring certainty. Natural disasters such as floods, unreasonable and narrow-minded political interference, proclamations about the impossibility of the project succeeding, and snide remarks about its viability — all of these steeled the team's resolve to keep moving forward.

The Nano has gone much beyond what Tata Motors had set out to achieve with it. The car has become a phenomenon and it has spawned a following across and beyond the automobile industry. But we can say with humility that the idea of the Nano has only begun to take root. We understand that it will take a lot more to make it a strong and healthy tree.

I am pleased that this book, which tells the story of the Nano, has been conceived and written. If it can help sow the seed or generate the spark for more innovative ideas, it would have greatly served its purpose. I am fortunate to have been associated with the Nano story and I consider it an honour to write this foreword.

Ravi Kant
Vice-Chairman, Tata Motors

CHAPTER **1**

The beginning

For people forced to flit from one serious business meeting to another, finding time to do their own thing can be difficult. So how do those who have to sit through countless such meetings deal with the tedium? Some doodle. That's what Ratan Tata — head of the Tata group of companies, India's largest and most respected business conglomerate — does sometimes to lift himself above the dreariness of administrative routine. From one such doodle was born the earliest idea of what would become the car that jolted the automobile world.

The Nano has been, and remains, essentially a product of Ratan Tata's imagination and his desire to recast the car as a means of affordable personal mobility for middle-class India. "It started by my spending a lot of time doodling at boring board meetings," he would recall years later at a gathering of Tata executives. "In other words, you have to be at boring meetings where you sit for long periods of time and can think of how you can make a difference to the world we live in. Most of us are victims of the environment in which we are and... we lose sight of the fact that we have a greater responsibility, a responsibility to serve the communities we live in, to improve the quality of life of the people we work with."

Coming from Ratan Tata, these thoughts convey the unshakeable belief of a standout business leader in an organisational ethos that places people and profitability on even pedestals. The Nano could not have been created, at least not in the manner it has been, in the absence of such faith and this philosophy of the enterprise.

"We are delighted in presenting the Tata Nano to India and the world." When Ratan Tata uttered those words at the launch of the Nano in Mumbai on March 23, 2009, it marked the apogee of a decade-long journey that had begun without any definite destination or coordinates, only a nebulous notion of engineering an automobile that would provide India with a reliable and affordable car. No one could have envisioned the nature of that journey: long and gruelling, exhilarating and heartbreaking, expensive and expansive, uplifted by the wonder of discovery and weighed down by the burden of breathing life into a radical concept.

At the core of the immense human endeavour to craft the Nano is Tata Motors, an automobile company whose employees believe they do more than just a job when they report for work. At its peak the Nano project had more than 500 people on its team. The most involved member of this team, the most zealous about realising its objective, was Ratan Tata, chairman of Tata Motors. The 72-year-old Ratan Tata is said to have the softest of corners for Tata Motors, the Tata enterprise closest to his heart. How it came to be that a Cornell-educated architect developed a passion for automobile engineering has never been satisfactorily explained, but it is clear enough that Ratan Tata had a dream of Tata Motors creating a 'people's car' many moons before the Nano project was put on track.

According to a magazine article, Ratan Tata thought up the Nano one day when he was caught in traffic in Bangalore and "noticed a single scooter carrying an entire family"[1]. That was far too facile to be true, but the family-on-the-scooter part was accurate enough. Ratan Tata first talked about the car as early as 2000, at a Tata Motors committee meeting. This was about a year after the company had launched the Indica, the first indigenous car to be made in India. "There has always been some sort of an unconscious urge to do something for the people of India and transport has been an area of interest," he said in a 2008 interview[2]. "As urbanisation gathers pace, personal transport has become a big issue, especially since mass transport is often not available or is of poor quality. Two-wheelers — with the father driving, the elder child standing in front and the wife behind holding a baby — is very much the norm in India. In that form two-wheelers are a relatively unsafe mode of transporting a family. The two-wheeler image is what got me thinking that we needed to create a safer form of transport."

Ratan Tata's initial doodle was to rebuild a car around the scooter, so that those using it could travel safer. He got in touch with an industry association and suggested a joint effort with Tata Motors to fashion what he termed an Asian car: large volumes, many countries involved and different people producing different sets of parts. The response was tepid. This was similar to what happened when Tata Motors wanted to make the Indica. Ratan Tata had proposed a partnership with an industry body to create an

Indian car, designed, developed and produced in the country, something that could be an Indian enterprise in its entirety. "Everybody scoffed," recalls Ratan Tata. "I remember people saying, 'Why doesn't Mr. Tata produce a car that works before he talks about an Indian car?'"

Others were even less complimentary, but that did not dilute the hope Tata Motors had of its small car. This could, the company's engineers felt, do for India what Ford's Model T did for Americans, the Fiat 500 for Italians, the Citroen 2CV for the French and the Volkswagen Beetle for the Germans. After all, India had been gradually shifting to the fast-growth highway ever since the economic reforms of the early 1990s, and a large number of its citizens were ready for a romance with cars.

There are some 600 million passenger cars on the world's roads today and the statistic is strengthened by about 67 million new units every year. Not surprisingly, the majority of these cars are in the developed world, and people in America, Europe and Japan own two-thirds of them. India and China, with more than a third of the world's population, have a mere 5 per cent of its vehicles. There are 5 million cars and 70 million two-wheelers in India, but only seven out of every 1,000 people in the country have a car, prompting *Forbes Asia* to write that "a billion Indians buy about the same number of cars in a year as 300-million Americans do in a month". That said, India's car market is expected to touch 2.2 million units a year by 2010[3]. The Nano was an initiative whose time had definitely come.

The success of the Indica — which debuted in 1998 and rode on the competence and resilience of Tata Motors at a time when the company had taken a body blow on revenues — gave Ratan Tata and his team the confidence to consider the extraordinary: a low-cost car that would shape the evolution of personal mobility in

India even as it adapted to the changing realities of a country on the move. Sure, some automobile engineering orthodoxies would have to be overcome, doubters within the organisation would need to be convinced, and a new kind of thinking would have to take root.

The Rs1-lakh cost that would come to define the Nano, was born of a casual comment Ratan Tata made at the Geneva Motor Show in 2003 (a lakh is the Indian nomenclature for a hundred thousand). During the course of an interview with the British newspaper, the *Financial Times*, he spoke in general terms about an affordable car being on Tata Motors' agenda for the future. Pressed on the cost of such a car, he said it could be around $2,500. The next morning the *Financial Times* had a story that the Tatas were planning to manufacture a Rs1-lakh car. Ratan Tata's gut reaction was to issue a rebuttal, to clarify that that was not quite what he had said. Then he thought that the figure had sprung from what he had indeed mentioned, "So why not just take that as a target?" The people at Tata Motors were aghast, but the company's chairman had his goal and his team a cost cast in concrete.

As the days went by almost every automobile industry professional, whether executive or expert, privately or publicly scorned the notion of a Rs1-lakh car. Osamu Suzuki, the chairman of Suzuki, the largest foreign car manufacturer in India, proclaimed that building a car at that cost was not possible, that it could never be made safe enough, and that it would be buried by the competition. Carlos Ghosn, who heads the Nissan-Renault combine, was among the rare few to differ with the crowd, understanding that a potential game-changer was on its way.

The cost element was what made Ratan Tata conceptualise, at the embryonic stage of the project, a 'rural car', a frugal automobile that would have to make do without doors and windows and probably have plastic curtains that rolled down. That would make it little more than a four-wheel version of the auto-rickshaw, a cheap and popular mode of transport in many parts of South and South East Asia. But as the idea of the Nano began to get crystallised, the engineers at Tata Motors realised that they would have to pack a more solid punch. Out went plastic curtains and the like and in came the thinking that this had to be a car as everyone expected a car to be, not some ersatz pretender. This was a shifting of goalposts that changed the essence of what the car would be, adding a new set of challenges to an already crowded cart.

So, now, in addition to the cost barrier there was the task of packing in more features and parts, the consequent inflationary pressures and substantial alterations in basic raw materials needed. For the team working on the project, this stage would in hindsight be among the easier to navigate because the concept of the car was still malleable, still in the process of being firmed up. There was a host of ideas flying about, many of them emerging from the hothouse of Ratan Tata's mind, among them a car created by engineering plastics and new materials, the use of aerospace adhesives instead of welding, and making one part perform multiple functions.

Some of these ideas would crash head-on against the harsh realities of cost-benefit analysis and, to paraphrase the British biologist Thomas Huxley, beautiful hypotheses would be slain by ugly fact. For instance, the plastics idea was discarded because painted plastics would have been more expensive than steel for the large volumes visualised for the small car. Huge production numbers were always part of the Nano equation. There was no way the car would succeed unless it targeted the wide base of the customer pyramid. Small would, in the context, be an adjective that applied only to the car's size. In all other respects this would have to be a big undertaking, especially on how many cars Tata Motors could produce in a year.

When the facilities for the car were being considered and a business plan chalked out, an early version shown to Ratan Tata settled for a production figure of 200,000 a year. The chairman was unimpressed. The way he saw it, if Tata Motors could pull this off it had to be looking at manufacturing a million cars a year — or none at all. A million cars of one model in a year? It had never been done in India, and doing it the conventional way would mean an investment of billions of dollars. That led Tata Motors to ponder options such as what it called distributed manufacturing, wherein a low-cost, low-breakeven-point production unit would be designed by the company and given to entrepreneurs willing to invest in a facility of this kind. Different ways of servicing the product were mulled, at the customer end and — borrowing from the insurance industry — having self-employed people trained and certified by the company.

The revolutionary and innovative were scripted into the Nano narrative all the way through, and not just in terms of engineering, design and cost. Tata Motors was in overdrive trying to make its baby a truly trailblazing product, not merely because that was the road to take, but out of the understanding that the breakthrough it had set sights on needed out-of-the-car thinking. The only thing clear and conventional in all of this, once the uncertainty of the early days had passed, was that the Nano would be a proper car, not an apology for one. As Ratan Tata said: "We were always conscious that there should be no quality stigma attached to the buying of this product. This was never going to be a half-car."

The minutes of a meeting involving Ratan Tata and the small-car team in April 2003 show the still exploratory nature of what was then called Project X3. Among the meeting notes were the development approach (upgrade the three-wheeler rather than downgrade the four-wheeler), DaimlerChrysler's struggles to design a family car for China, tubular frames and laser welding, the possibility of hand painting the car and having staggered seating, even producing the vehicle without doors. The meeting closed with Ratan Tata suggesting that the team work full-time on the project over the following six months, and assuring additional resources wherever required.

The fluid and as yet indeterminate nature of the project was also reflected in the composition of the team working on it. Based at Tata Motors' Engineering Research Centre in Pune, it comprised five people drawn from different engineering disciplines, each reporting to his departmental head. What made the task at hand tougher for these engineers was the absence of any benchmarks against which to place the product. They would have to find their own point of reference and appropriate yardsticks from within. But there were some broad guidelines to work with.

The way Ratan Tata had thought of the small car, it would have fewer parts than a conventional automobile and these parts would have to be easy to assemble. That's where the distributed manufacturing suggestion came in: have a mother plant where the important components are made and transport these to satellite sites where the assembling could take place. This would mean channel partners, the generation of jobs across the country, greater customisation of the car and a slashing of logistics costs. It was a pathbreaking concept, but the potential for problems to arise and the difficulties of assuring consistency in quality meant that it would be kept aside for exploration at a later date. As with many of the other ideas associated with the project, the distributed manufacturing model was mooted and pursued because of the cost reductions it promised.

The cost factor initially resulted in the suggestion of a car without doors, but with just some kind of safety bars, and from there to having soft shutters for protection against the elements. Another option mooted was a motorised quadricycle, a four-wheeled bicycle. Look at the first lot of styling sketches of the car and it has almost nothing in common with the Nano. The reason was simple: making a watered-down car never did make sense, common or business. This logic also underpinned the performance criteria of the car, its engine, safety norms and emissions, all of which had to be up to regulatory and other standards. There would be no cutting of corners here — on that Ratan Tata was clear.

Ratan Tata has a sharp sense of what customers want, an attribute accentuated, in this instance, by his understanding and knowledge of all things motoring. In the event, his experience of driving the very first version of the small car that his engineers rigged up was deflating. This happened sometime in early 2005 at the Tata Motors test track in Pune, and the mule, as it is called in automobile parlance, was as crude as its moniker. The car had been fitted with a single-cylinder engine sourced from the local market and was, as those present remember it, as sophisticated as a jalopy. How Ratan Tata settled his big frame into the contraption is a mystery, but there was no doubting his state of mind after he got himself out of the car. "I should not have driven this," he said.

These initial days, as is typical in such a project, were filled with disappointments and the despair caused by delays. The drive in the uninspiring mule convinced Ratan Tata that his small car would have to be the real deal, with more-than-enough engineering to entice customers and enough juice to keep them coming back for more. Success would depend, he rightly figured, in managing to pull this off within the cost limit he had inadvertently set. A few months later, Ratan Tata got to drive a second version of the small car, this one with a proper two-cylinder engine that had been developed in-house at the Tata Motors facility in Pune. It was better — it had to be — but still needed improving. This is one example of the step-by-painful-step, target-oriented development process that would become integral to the small-car project.

The project started with a clean canvas and no benchmarks, but there's no denying that everyone at Tata Motors, including the chairman, knew their small car would have to stand comparison with the Maruti-800, a blockbuster product that had changed middle India's impression of a car. The Maruti had been around for 25 years and was still in the driver's seat in terms of sales. To take on and beat this runaway leader, the Nano would have to be an improvement on factors such as acceleration, drive comfort, space and looks. And this had to be managed at less than half the cost of the competitor.

The Maruti-800 may have been a back-of-the mind target, but the Tata Motors small car was always running its own race. Its performance goals were never set in stone, which resulted in the car forever evolving, getting more refined as the days rolled by and enduring the severest of scrutiny, most so by the person who had given his heart to the project.

Ratan Tata, an automobile maven by inclination and a company chairman by circumstance, has been from day one the force behind the small-car project. He has been the bond that has united a band of engineers and professionals from disparate functions in realising a cherished goal, encouraging and cajoling, pushing and prodding, praising and criticising a team for whom he came to represent the epitome of leadership. Yet, according to those who worked with him, Ratan Tata was always more of a team player than a captain in this endeavour, rolling up his sleeves and immersing himself in shop-floor details and engineering minutiae as the small car took shape.

To appreciate the depth of Ratan Tata's involvement in the small-car project, it may be necessary to understand the relationship that developed between him and the young engineers in Pune. To begin with, they reacted with awe to his presence, treating with near-reverence the stately and urbane father-figure who had chosen to spend his precious time with them and away from the business of heading a conglomerate with over 98 companies and more than 350,000 people under its umbrella.

This unequal association would over time mature into a mutual feeling of faith and solidarity, the kind of kinship that sailors on long voyages come to share. This was not an interaction marked by emails and phone calls; rather, it grew over numerous face-to-face meetings in a work environment where the one-for-all, all-for-one sentiment was dominant. With every challenge that the project faced, every roadblock that had to be overcome, the relationship was strengthened, to a point where Ratan Tata began being treated — not without some bit of effort on his part — as another member of the small-car team.

Ratan Tata was game for get-togethers with the professionals at the Pune and other Tata Motors facilities before the small-car project was put on track. The way he saw it, interacting with the best young talent in the company without the crutch of presentations and away from conference rooms was an enlightening effort for both parties. Most of these meetings, a tradition that began in the early 2000s, took place at Lake House, a green haven set in a sylvan glade near the Tata Motors plant in Pune. There was no agenda or food-chain hierarchies for the interactions, which involved open-house and informal discussions with groups of 10-15 people in the 25-35 age band. All that the engineers had to bring along was an open mind, though there is little doubt they would have deposited at the door all the riches they possessed for a chance to meet their chairman.

As C Ramakrishnan, the chief financial officer at Tata Motors, remembers it, the get-togethers would start at around 7pm and stretch to midnight and beyond. The discussions would get animated as the night wore on, particularly so at Ratan Tata's table, with lots of give and take and not a few disagreements. The talking points centred on motoring and the automobile industry, and the chairman was at least as conversant about the subject as the professionals he was matching minds with. His background in architecture may have helped, but there has always been a side of Ratan Tata that understood cars from the perspective of a customer and a connoisseur, in design and development, technical specifications and overall packaging. This knowledge would prove vital as the small-car project progressed.

The customer tended, in the days before the Indian economy was opened up, to be taken for granted, if not for a ride. Tata Motors was not the only guilty party; this was the way it was, not just in the automobile industry but across the spectrum. Ratan Tata, it can be said, did more than anyone in the organisation he headed to change an attitude that smacked of superciliousness. Much of his criticism of the way Tata Motors operated was directed at getting rid of the arrogance towards those whose patronage sustains you, and instilling an outward-looking attitude.

The first project that benefited in full measure from this change of outlook and behaviour within Tata Motors was the Ace, a customer-focused mini truck launched in May 2005. The Ace transformed the light commercial vehicles market in India, tapping into a customer base hungry for a goods carrier of the kind and selling in excess of 100,000 units within 20 months of its launch.

The small-car project drew on a raft of lessons learned during the development of the Ace, especially in comprehending and respecting what the market wanted, and would, in time, come to be headed by the same engineer who navigated the mini truck to success, Girish Wagh, a soft-spoken, hard-driven workaholic with extensive expertise in all things motoring and an outstanding people manager. But there was a lot of ground that was covered prior to that happening, and the primary facilitator in the period leading up to Wagh's appointment was Ramakrishnan. He recalls the small car as being the holy grail at that point, within Tata Motors and in the car industry, almost mythical in terms of what it had set out to achieve.

Ramakrishnan was then a member of Ratan Tata's core team at Bombay House, the Tata group headquarters in Mumbai. His was the responsibility of arranging periodic meetings in Pune between the chairman and the small-car team, of trouble-shooting and listening to what the engineers were saying. This was 2003 and the Nano was still very much in its nascent stage, with early evaluations of technical specifications and long debates on design, material and the like. The small-car team had people from engineering, sourcing and planning, handpicked talent with the best of capabilities; by the start of 2004 its strength had increased to 12.

Everything was up for discussion, with Ratan Tata in attendance at all the important meetings (Ramakrishnan remembers four in which the chairman heard arguments for and against using plastic parts instead of metal). Progress was dreadfully slow, it was all taking too long and Ratan Tata was getting impatient. There were fundamental issues to be resolved, values to be defined, deliverables to be secured, and results to be evaluated. This was not unusual for a project so vast in scope and challenge — the Ace went through a longer gestation period — but that did not make it any easier for the chairman to accept. It did not help that the list of naysayers and doubters inside the company was growing by the day, though the small-car team itself never wavered in its conviction.

One example of the laboriousness of the process concerns engine performance and fuel efficiency. The Tata small car had to, the case went, be significantly superior to the Maruti 800 on both counts, or it would not make sense for a scooter or motorcycle owner to consider buying one. Ramakrishnan, a chartered accountant roped in to administer and organise an engineering process, survived this first phase on hope and desire, and the belief that with Ratan Tata in the thick of things nothing was impossible.

If it's Saturday it must be Pune — that became the ritual for Ramakrishnan over the 18 months prior to Wagh taking charge of the project. He would sit with the team, the engineers and the others, organise support services, talk to the sourcing people, review what had been done and head back to Mumbai to update the chairman. It was exasperating at times, given the sluggish pace of progress, and what he had to tell Ratan Tata was more unsatisfactory than satisfactory. That did not faze Ratan Tata, a man for whom perseverance and commitment mean the world, but his frustration was evident to Ramakrishnan. Being critical without offering a solution is not his style, so he was always there with an alternative when any pathway got closed.

"If he is unhappy about an outcome he'll give you a direction," says Ramakrishnan. "'Have you looked at it this way? Can we do it in this fashion?' It's the kind of reaction that reassures people and energises them. There were occasions when he got back to us a day after a meeting and said: 'You know, a thought came to my mind about yesterday. We missed something there. Maybe we should look at the problem differently.' And he never blows his top. At the same time, if he is also unhappy he will let you know. This is an extremely transparent person. Whether he is praising you or is upset with you, he never lacks clarity. We got the impression during those days that for him it was a series of disappointments, but we did have some good interactions, too."

It has been said that when you buy a car you are mostly paying for the knowledge embedded in its design, not the metal and glass. By that measure Nikhil Atmaram Jadhav, an industrial designer by designation and a design devotee by disposition, would qualify as a vital member of the Nano team. A 30-something engineer who joined Tata Motors eight years back fresh out of a postgraduate course in design from the Indian Institute of Technology in Mumbai, Jadhav was part of a four-member advanced engineering group that joined the small-car project in December 2002. The project had been on for about a year by then, with a skeletal team and not much progress to show. The need for a momentum surge, a speeding up of the learning process, was being felt.

The advanced engineering group, which included Jay Bolar from Tata Motors' Engineering Research Centre, vehicle safety specialist Anil Kumar C and RG Rajhans from body systems engineering, had been set up to consider engineering options for a small car, in terms of size and the space inside, weight and engine, design, material and the rest. The members of the group, all then in their twenties and dealing directly with the top management, were not told specifically about the small-car project, but what they did and learned would be handy once it gathered steam.

Jadhav had been drafted into the team to explore design and styling options for a barebones city car. He was flummoxed initially, and had no clue about what to refer to and where to start. The placing of the engine had not been fixed, the number of doors had not been decided and no price had been mentioned; the only certainty was that the car would be low on cost and without any frills. The design effort began with sketches and a package layout, jargon for how to place different elements inside the vehicle. The advanced engineering boys played around with the configuration of the engine and decided to put it in the rear, freeing up utility space in front. That's how the first mule, the one that would dishearten Ratan Tata, came into being, with objects crudely packed into what looked like a rudimentary car.

Prior to this, one evening in early 2003, Jadhav and his colleagues from the advanced engineering group in Pune were told they had to meet Ratan Tata at Bombay House the next morning. The engineers were nervous; they did not have much to show to the chairman and even less to talk about. Ratan Tata put them at ease at the meeting, held at the Tata Motors conference room on the first floor of the Tata headquarters, saying he wanted a discussion rather than a presentation. He was not certain about what he wanted, but he was clear about what he did not want the small car to be. He was also keen that the group explore every avenue in the development process, even the most unconventional, suggesting, for instance, that they look at furniture catalogues before deciding how the car's seating could be styled and positioned. The message was unambiguous: break out of the mould.

That was easier said than done. The first mule had an 8.5 horsepower engine and was white in colour and had inputs on styling from the Italian design house IDEA (Institute of Development in Automotive Engineering), which would play an important role in the way the Nano eventually turned out. The cheaper frame-construction method was chosen instead of the robotics-heavy monocoque technique, and three concepts were presented. The one that looked most like a car was picked for development, with Ratan Tata's approval, and the refining of the design got underway. The exterior design signoff happened in early 2005 and a model made of inorganic wood, with the glass openings blackened out, was milled from a computer-aided design (CAD). This was reviewed on April 1, 2005, and, though not the finished article, it looked far from foolish.

This wood model was never going to be acceptable, simply because actual rendering is a world apart in detailing from CAD outputs. Styling tapes, so called because they are pasted on to define new design lines, were put on the model. The interior design had not even begun — this starts in a car development programme about six months after the exterior is completed — but from the outside the car was being chiselled into shape. New features and lines were being continually introduced and the price barrier was in place by now, adding to the design team's how-do-we-do-it worries. For example, a vertical headlight panel design had been presented to Ratan Tata, who pushed for a horizontal configuration. The vertical would be the final choice, helping give the car the distinctive look it now sports.

The second mule, a grey number with windows and windshield still blacked out, had more detailing and richness in design. Justyn Norek, an Italian designer attached to IDEA, was playing a lead role in the development process at this point. He, Jadhav and others would collectively create a new style language for Tata Motors, more attractive, more modern and one that came to be used in the Nano and newer models of the Indica. Norek would spend a week of every month in India to do the primary designing, Jadhav would do the developing and finishing and they would then work together on finalisation. The CAD work was progressing while a new model was being readied and, in February 2006, Norek and Jadhav had, in design terms, a near-complete car to present to the chairman.

Further refining would happen before, in July 2006, an almost-final version of the small car was completed. Ratan Tata was not convinced. He thought the car looked too blunt and suggested that its nose portion be stretched forward slightly. That idea was incorporated and the chairman had the design he wanted. Whatever tinkering in styling happened after this was too minor for the uninitiated to notice. Ratan Tata's elegant sense of design had contributed in a big way to the Nano's final appearance, and the design team that executed his vision had a product they could justifiably be proud of.

The engineering package of the small car, suspension, engine and the rest, was running on a parallel track while the design was taking shape. The heart of the small car, its engine, was always going to be critical to its success, and deciding what best suited an optimal cost-to-performance equation was a long and laborious process. The way Sam Johnny, a mechanical engineer who joined Tata Motors in 1996, recalls the early search for an engine for the small car, the effort was marked with uncertainty and disappointment.

Johnny came to the small-car team in end-2003 after responding to an internal Tata Motors recruitment call for young engineers to join the project. There were 40 applicants and Johnny, who had been part of the Indica development programme, was one of two engineers selected. Very little aside from the cost barrier had been decided, though some broad conceptual themes had been placed on the table. Johnny's immediate task was to scout for information on engines and transmission systems. The internet was an important source for data and he frequently found himself spending his after-office hours in cyber cafes.

Johnny and his colleagues — there were some 10 people in the small-car team then — looked at small cars and small engines from around the world, with new and old technology, proprietary and those for sale. Calls were made and contact established with engine vendors in, among other places Australia, Italy and the United Sates. The plan at the time was to get a readymade engine rather than manufacture it at Tata Motors. Seven potential sources were considered, but the fit never happened: the engine was either too big or lacked in fuel-efficiency, some were counted out on cost and others got rejected for manufacturing complications. This went on for a year, near to the end of 2004, when the call was taken that Tata Motors would design and manufacture the engine in-house.

The disenchantment of a fruitless search was alleviated by the knowledge gained by the team members during its course; they now had a comprehensive understanding of engines and what was available in the market. A petrol engine was chosen principally due to the lower cost. It would be a two-cylinder version with an aluminium casting. The big discovery, though, was about the engine itself. The engineers on the Ace project had sliced a diesel engine in two to power the mini truck. For the Nano, the development team came up with a completely new design.

Reward for endeavours of another variety arrived on the safety system and structure for the small car, an area that was Anil Kumar's domain. Kumar, a 15-year veteran with Tata Motors, juggled responsibilities to make his contribution to the Nano's development, working after office hours when his bosses said he might have too much on his plate to concentrate his energies on the small car. The challenge of helping craft something new and exciting was what got him to bite, and this challenge was multiplied when Ratan Tata made his Geneva statement on the car's price. The advanced engineering guys were formally inducted into the small-car project and Kumar now had to work overtime handling a single responsibility.

By the summer of 2005, Ratan Tata had become convinced that the small-car project needed a fillip, probably with a different sort of leadership. The project team had made the hard yards and much progress had been achieved, but there seemed to be an intangible deficiency dragging the small car into delay. The chairman felt this drag more than anyone else, and it had begun to show in his demeanour. Tata Motors had just got a new managing director in Ravi Kant, till then the head of the company's commercial vehicles division, and he noticed the chairman's discontent with the way things were on the project. The time for a decisive shifting of gears had come, he was certain.

Kant had been on the sidelines of the small-car project up to that point, sitting in on some meetings and giving the occasional input. The Ace project was his baby and he had been instrumental in identifying Girish Wagh's potential and persuading the young engineer to head its development programme back in December 2000. That's the sort of leadership the small-car project needs, Kant figured. In August 2005, he had Wagh transferred from the Ace to the Nano and also effected a couple of other changes. When he informed Ratan Tata about these decisions, he saw a gleam in the chairman's eyes. "He thought new life had been injected into the project, that a turning point had been reached," Kant recalls. "Even at that stage it was not a certainty that the small car would see the light of day. Now those doubts were put to rest."

The die was cast: Kant would drive the project, Wagh would lead it and Ratan Tata would oversee it all. Wagh had been reluctant to join the Ace team, immersed as he was then in the Tata Business Excellence Model (TBEM), a group-wide business improvement programme that has fetched tremendous gains for companies following its guidelines. But when the Nano offer came his way, he was more than willing to oblige. Wagh's hesitancy on the Ace was due to the depth of his involvement in the TBEM initiative, which, as he saw it, had given him access to different Tata companies and their functioning, and knowledge of a range of industry segments.

It was through TBEM, indeed, that Wagh first came to Kant's notice. This happened in the beginning of 2000, when Wagh was a member of the team assessing Tata Steel on the TBEM scale and Kant was a judge of the process. Kant was impressed with the passion the young appraiser exuded. He pulled Wagh aside and asked him to come and work in his office in Mumbai. "I'd rather work on an independent assignment out of Pune," said Wagh in response. A few months passed and Kant sought out the reticent engineer once again, offering him the opportunity of leading the Ace project. Wagh, neck-deep in a quality improvement initiative at Tata Motors, tried saying no once again. The negative would not pass this time.

A blend of cajoling and hectoring by Kant got Wagh to change his mind, but not before a bit of drama. "Deny me again and I will conclude that there's this man who does not want to come to the forefront, who is averse to taking on challenging roles," Kant said. That hurt enough for Wagh to say, "I'll be at your service from tomorrow morning." So, in December 2000, the Ace project found an ace of its own and the path was paved for Wagh to discover that there's more to business than excellence.

Wagh had met Ratan Tata for the first time in 2000 as a 29-year-old, at one of the Lake House meetings that Ramakrishnan used to organise. This was a dinner affair and a debate got started about cost cutting at Tata Motors. An argument was made about separating the transmission and axle divisions from the mother company. Wagh countered the view and his animated response caught the chairman's attention. Ratan Tata intervened and said, "Don't worry, I won't be selling [the divisions] tomorrow." He then gave Wagh his telephone number and urged him to call if ever he felt the need to.

Some four years later, in late 2003, Wagh had another chance to interact directly with the chairman, this time as the leader of a TBEM assessment team at a presentation to the board of Tata Power. Presentation done with, Wagh was asked by Ratan Tata to meet him at his office. Thrilled to bits, Wagh spent 45 minutes with a person he seems to admire and adore in equal measure. Ratan Tata gave him a couple of tips on how his presentation could have been improved, discussed the then underway Ace project and, at the end, enquired if he might like to get involved, probably even lead, the small-car team. Nothing much happened on the last point for the next 18 months, but the story shows that getting Wagh on board the project may not have been an out-of-the-blue decision.

Wagh would eventually move to the small-car programme in August 2005, in the same month that Ravi Kant took over as the managing director of Tata Motors. The freshly appointed boss remembered what had happened on the last occasion he made Wagh an offer he could refuse. This time he cut off all escape routes, no doubt to spare both parties any unnecessary dramatics. "Girish," he said, "I'm going to tell you something and you can only listen. You are being moved, with immediate effect, to the small-car project. You will lead the team and report directly to me. And you will have to interact a lot with the chairman." Wagh was quiet. So, what do you think, he was asked. "You told me I could not speak." Wagh was not so quiet three days later, when Ratan Tata, on one of his visits to the Pune plant to track the project, shook his hand and thanked him for joining the team.

Wagh did plenty more speaking in the days ahead as he started coming to grips with the gargantuan challenge laid out before him. The good part was that he had the managing director and the chairman to lean on, that he could count on their support in the face of failure. Yes, it was difficult to get people who did not report to him to follow his instructions, as it was to convince team members to pull their weight rather than tell them to do so. The sentiment soon turned positive for the team and the project, for Wagh and the two men who had placed their faith in him.

Kant's contribution in easing the small car's troubles was at least as important as the day-to-day problem solving that Wagh had to do. He, more than anyone, helped knock down the walls that had made Tata Motors a hierarchy-bound organisation, and in this he had the steadfast support of Prakash Telang, the veteran engineer who would become the company's managing director for India operations in August 2009. Kant understood the criticality of hacking down hesitancy and scepticism, of eliminating bureaucratic layers and sending out the signal loud and clear that creating the small car was an organisational goal. And Ratan Tata's project to boot.

The entire concept of what would become the Nano got transformed over the course of its development. Even before the troubles to come — the forced shift from Singur to Sanand, the political and other controversies — increased the degree of difficulty the project had to deal with, there were other booby traps to navigate around. Commodity prices had gone through the roof from the time when Ratan Tata made the Rs1-lakh commitment, a whole lot of time had elapsed since the project was started, the team's composition and leadership had seen change, and evolving regulatory norms put further pressures on the cost front. The price promise was probably the only constant here and Kant made sure nobody forgot it, in one instance even threatening to abandon the project if the costing equation got skewed.

Ramakrishnan, the facilitator of the early days, eased himself out of the project as Kant and Wagh took charge. Saturdays, for him, would no longer have a Pune flavour. As for the Nano — which means small in Gujarati, the language of the state where the car eventually found a home, as well as in English, and originates from the Greek root nanos, or dwarf — the challenges would get gigantic in the days ahead. Some of these were foreseen, others could not have been. It would require more than Gandhian engineering, a terminology that first appeared in *The New York Times*, to overcome the hurdles and deliver a car that India and Indians could take to heart.

For inspiration, if nothing else, there was the Ford Model T to look up to. Launched in 1908 at a cost of $850 (about $20,000, or Rs1 million, in 2009 terms), it had a 20-horsepower, four-cylinder engine, a top speed of 45mph and fuel economy of 15-20 to the gallon. By the mid-1920s the Model T's price was down to $260, it had changed the way people thought about personal transport, laid the seeds for the enduring love affair between human beings and cars, and, some would argue, altered the course of capitalism. No wonder, then, the affection it evoked. In 'Farewell, my Lovely!', a brilliant elegy to the Model T penned for the *New Yorker* magazine in 1936, EB White was besotted enough to write: "I can still feel my old Ford nuzzling me at the curb, as though looking for an apple in my pocket."

Henry Ford, with some help from his workers, produced more than 15 million Model Ts in 20 years, became rich enough to be worth $190 billion in today's money, and ruthlessly realistic to thunder, "History is more or less bunk. It is tradition. We want to live in the present, and the only history that is worth a tinker's damn is the history we make today." Ratan Tata is also a realist, but more sentimental than tough old Henry and decidedly more appreciative of the past. There is a thread, though, that connects the two motorcar men through the ages. As the writer Sean O'Grady[4] would say, the Nano is Ratan Tata's "flattering tribute to the abiding power of Ford's vision".

CHAPTER **2**

The challenges

"I don't think any undertaking in the history of automobile manufacturing has had to deal with as many challenges as the
Nano project." Hear Ravi Kant, not a man given to exaggeration, make this statement and you begin to understand what Tata
Motors had to endure over the course of nearly a decade to realise
its small-car goal. As Kant, the company's managing director during a critical period of the Nano's development, lists these challenges, it becomes clear that engineering the car was a task lesser
in magnitude than coping with the extraneous elements which
dragged the project into delay and those united behind it into
something close to despair.

On the engineering front, the big challenges that confronted
the Nano team were finding suitable design solutions, getting the

engineering package right and managing all of this within extremely stringent cost parameters. These challenges were often interrelated, with decisions in one sphere affecting the other two. The greater test came bearing malice and machinations: the partisan opposition that led to Tata Motors being forced to shut its plant at Singur in West Bengal, the rush to quickly find another place for the facility, dismantling the original production infrastructure and shifting it to a new location at Sanand in Gujarat, and establishing interim manufacturing capabilities at Pantnagar in Uttarakhand.

The 'external' troubles to come were some way in the distance when Kant took charge of the Nano development programme and, in August 2005, roped in a young and dynamic engineer named Girish Wagh to head it. The project had been meandering along and was in need of a fillip. Kant, a grizzled veteran of several corporate and marketing battles, and Wagh, a leader waiting to be discovered, would together provide the ballast that steadied the small-car project and set it on course for conclusion.

To start with, Wagh had a core team of six engineers to drive the project, along with people from Tata Motors' Engineering Research Centre (ERC) and the sourcing function. He also had backing from the very top, from Tata Motors chairman Ratan Tata, and the support of an organisation with extensive, if scattered, engineering knowledge. Wagh would come to depend on seasoned hands such as Prakash Telang, currently managing director for India operations, and Ramesh Akarte as the project gathered pace.

Akarte, a mentor and guide to Wagh during his early growth phase in the company, then headed ERC. He had been pulled into the project a few months before Wagh joined it and his contribution soon become invaluable. "His being there was a big boost," Wagh would recall. "He had this ability to take decisions at any level of engineering, to calm our team and give us confidence."

Confidence was critical at this stage of the project. Decisions could not be postponed, as had been happening in the initial, conceptualisation stage. There was an urgency in the air, accentuated by Ratan Tata's increasingly frequent presence at reviews. "We wanted to get a move on," recalls Wagh. "The time for debate and doing things on paper had passed. We knew the worse that could happen was that we would fail. That did not matter."

The styling of the car was not yet final, but Wagh and his engineers went ahead and started making a prototype. This was not an easy decision to make, with some members of the team reckoning that Ratan Tata had to freeze the design before further work on the car began. Akarte and Wagh thought differently and by December 2005 they had a car for Ratan Tata to try out. The chairman was not quite convinced; he thought the car lacked in acceleration. Out went the 543cc engine, to be replaced by one with a 586cc capacity and the realisation that the Nano had to be better than the redoubtable Maruti-800, on this and every other count.

The new small-car prototype had a continuously variable transmission system — the gearless car, for the uninitiated — but the acceleration here, too, did not satisfy the stickler in Tata. That's when Wagh and Akarte opted for a regular four-speed manual transmission. Kant wanted the new transmission system ready in three months, a tough time frame in which to design from scratch, manufacture and put it in the car. "We did it in four months," says Wagh, "from nothing to getting it fixed in the car." An alpha prototype with the manual transmission system was shown to Ratan Tata in August 2006. "He said there was improvement, but not enough. Performance, power, acceleration — we needed to get better everywhere."

The "getting better" part was not so much about pleasing the chairman as it was about living up to the expected demands of the fickle Indian customer. A 623cc engine was crafted and another prototype readied by early 2007. A flurry of other activity was happening while this engine was refined: setting up at Singur, evaluating equipment and technology for manufacturing, tying up with suppliers, looking at tooling and ordering dies. A final prototype was produced by July 2007 and this one got Ratan Tata's nod. Work on the engine would not end there and, consequently, what sits in the back of the Nano today is a vastly superior piece of engineering craftsmanship with, in Wagh's words, "hundreds of improvements".

Ratan Tata had, in the meantime, been pushing for loose ends on other aspects of the project to be tied up. Wagh was worried about plans for the plant being delayed as the team strove to get the car and its coordinates in order, but that was not really a concern for the chairman. As early as November 2005, right after Wagh had been made the project head, Ratan Tata said in a conversation, "Mark my words, it will be the product that controls the timeline, not the manufacturing facility." He would, in hindsight, turn out to be right and wrong, but who was to know then what twists and turns lay in store?

By mid-2007, though, it was still about stretching every sinew to reach targets, and then setting fresh ones. To meet the Rs1-lakh target the small-car team had to rigorously enforce a cost code across the project, on the product and its parts, materials and manufacturing facilities, logistics and customer support. Wagh uses the term "brainstorming" to describe the long and physically draining meetings that preceded decision-making. "We demanded a high level of perseverance from our people and we got it."

This was a bit more problematic than it sounds. The designing of a product or a process in automobile manufacturing is a creative endeavour, and a time-consuming one at that. Exhaustion levels are inevitably high, and these can become unbearable when rework and rejection become the norm. "To tell somebody, after all the effort he has put in, that it's no good, that he has to produce something better, and to do this five-six times, over and over again — it's a humungous task, not so much physically as psychologically," says Wagh. So what made the Nano team cope? "Commitment, for sure, and the absence of any fear of failure. They knew they may not achieve their target, but they would have got closer to it."

The styling of the Nano exemplifies the stretched targets that characterised the development of the small car. This had been finalised in July 2006, but Ratan Tata thought the look of the front portion of the car was rather abrupt. With time constraints coming to a head, his concern was that any further design suggestions from his side would delay the project. But the development team and Ravi Kant were in agreement with the chairman that the front look needed to change, and so it happened that 50mm were added to the Nano's nose. This was a minuscule alteration, but its effect on the car's overall appearance was significant. The tough part was getting the new nose in place.

Nikhil Jadhav, the design torchbearer, and his mates had to work 20-hour days to finish the nose job and complete in two weeks a task that would ordinarily have taken up to a month. This because, while the increase in length may seem minor to the outsider, it affected the car's lamps, its wheel base and its entire structure. Ratan Tata was satisfied with the outcome and Jadhav merely relieved when, in late August 2006, the new design got a sign-off. It had been a long and taxing journey and a model of the car could now be created.

A computer-aided design rendering of the entire vehicle was completed and the actual engineering of it began in right earnest. This is akin to what a civil engineer does with a building, working on the design drawn up by the architect. The civil engineer has to decide what is, from an engineering standpoint, feasible, what is too expensive to do and what cannot be done. The design team of the Nano project had finished 'architecting' the car, and now the engineering people got on the job of building it. This is when, typically, discoveries are made about what is possible and what isn't. For instance, the air scoops at the side of the car, which carry air to the engine, had to be changed. When air conditioning was added, an opening had to be fashioned in the front of the car. The bumper was altered to integrate fog lamps into it.

As the idea took hold that the Nano could mean different things to different people, with extra features, customised accessories and such for high-end models, the engineering of the car got more complex and the product a lot richer in terms of comfort and quality. The physical crafting of the car had started in early 2007 and continued right up to the time it was unveiled at the Delhi Auto Expo in January 2008. No detail was too small for Ratan Tata to notice and no task too taxing for his team to accomplish.

This is particularly so with the car's interior, where design elements and the number of materials used far exceeded what appeared on its exterior portion. Two design themes were developed concurrently for the Nano's interior, one by the Italian design house, IDEA, and the other by the Tata Motors design team. This because, while IDEA was working with inputs from Pune, the small-car team thought its own design people had a better understanding of the Indian market and its requirements. The competition this arrangement bred was healthy enough for elements from the designs of both teams to be meshed and blended for the final model.

Cost was a constant consideration. That's why the dashboard designed by the Tata Motors' team was discarded in favour of IDEA's integrated console, and neither design had a lockable storage space. Cost was also the reason why, initially, the car had a headrest that was built into the seat. Ratan Tata thought this gave the inside a crowded feeling, which was when a headrest with a hollow came in. All inside trims, plastic design elements that enhance the looks of the interior, had to serve a purpose. Nothing for fancy's sake anywhere, though it was clear from the beginning that the two versions at the higher end would have more features than the base model. This meant, for example, different steering wheels and floor consoles.

Seven show cars were made for the unveiling at the Auto Expo and it was no easy task. These cars did not come off an assembly line; they were built in a prototype shop at the Engineering Research Centre in Pune, piece by piece, and it took a lot of discipline and care for detail. Secrecy was paramount. The cars were put together in a cordoned-off area where mobile phones and cameras were not allowed. "You couldn't enter the place without signing a ledger and proving you were a part of the development team," recalls Jadhav, one of about hundred Tata Motors people with access to the high-security zone. "We often worked through the night. Other times we would be there till midnight and come back at 6am. There was this amazing spirit."

Jadhav is philosophical about the huge amount of design work and rework that went into the creation of the Nano. "You can't be subjective about design, you can't impose your views and you can't do a car in isolation. You might be the one who came up with the sketch, but to convert it to a car you require 100-200 people. You have to play in the team, yet you have to guard the interest of your domain." Inputs were taken and assimilated, and opinions from every level of the development team, chairman to shop-floor engineer, were considered. "There were occasions when we had something we thought was great, but it could not be manufactured, and with good reason. The single, overriding factor in all of this was the customer. We always held him up as the final benefactor."

So what was the experience like? "When I think of the Nano project," says Jadhav, "I don't see it as a project, not at all. It was an exploration."

The Indica and Ace projects, which preceded the development of the Nano, had taught Tata Motors lessons in engineering that it could not have otherwise learned. A 'new product introduction' (NPI) process had been put in place following the niggling hassles that came in the wake of the launch of the first batch of the Indica back in 1998. Ratan Tata had brought in the Warwick Manufacturing Group (now called WMG), part of the School of Engineering at the University of Warwick in Britain, to help Tata Motors get its engineering equations right. The NPI process was a direct outcome of WMG's intervention and opened many eyes across the Tata Motors organisation about what it lacked.

"To be honest, we have still not implemented WMG's recommendations to the fullest extent, but thanks to them we now know how product development and introduction should be managed," says Girish Wagh, one of many hundreds of Tata Motors engineers who benefited from the engagement. "That was a fantastic learning for all of us. It wasn't so much about management or processes as it was about core engineering."

This core engineering expertise came in handy when the engine of the Nano was being developed. Ratan Tata was clear that the small-car team should not build the car around whatever engine it opted for; that would be, he said, like stitching a shirt around a button. The Nano's engine sits in the back, not unique for a car — the Volkswagen Beetle, for example, has such a layout — but certainly different. This decision, taken early on in the project and before Wagh came into the picture, would deliver some useful advantages while also posing its share of problems. The engineering maturity now inculcated in Tata Motors ensured that the advantages were seized and the problems settled with aplomb.

The back-engine layout was purely an efficient packaging solution. It released significant space inside the Nano, one reason why it is about 20 per cent bigger on the inside than the Maruti-800, and gave the car a larger crumple zone, the area that absorbs the impact of a crash. However, it brought with it challenges in handling and stability. The handling issues were sorted out by moving some aggregates to the front portion of the vehicle, fine-tuning the front suspension system and tweaking the arrangement of the tyres. The tall-boy design, with its higher centre of gravity, was stabilised by placing the battery under the driver's seat and the spare wheel in the boot, which was in the front.

Despite the solutions, doubts lingered about the rear-engine idea. Would it heat up the cabin? Would the noise and vibration levels be over the threshold? "We were forever challenging traditional automobile engineering concepts," says Wagh. "Trial and error became the norm." Ratan Tata and Ravi Kant were hands on during this stage of the project, and their involvement was of immense help to the young engineers burning calories and midnight oil to realise an objective that had by now captured the imagination of the entire organisation.

The core team itself was too busy with the nitty-gritty to get carried away by the attention the Nano project was attracting. GR Nagabhushan, a testing specialist attached to Tata Motors' Engineering Research Centre, remembers getting into repeated arguments with the car's designers. "We were the conscience keepers of the project and we pored over the minutest of details during our testing cycles," he says. "We kept evaluating the product in the context of the market, in the context of the customer." The testing team dug up issues of over-design, of flab and unnecessary frills. This made them less than popular with some members of the larger development team, but that was an inconvenience that came with the testing territory.

Everything was put under the scanner. Why four doors, for example, when a survey had revealed that people use the right-rear door only about 5 per cent of the time? Get rid of it and cost would come down. Ratan Tata did not agree. "That would be perceived as a compromise," he insisted, sticking to his conviction that the Nano needed to have all that a proper car did. The chairman was more accommodating in the matter of tyres, which are of different sizes in the front and back. Most cars have four tyres of the same size, but the Nano's front tyres are smaller than its back tyres. This is to offset the extra weight of the engine at the back, balance the handling of the car and improve its overall dynamics. Another challenge was the braking system, which is, again, different from those in other cars.

"We went back to the drawing board so many times that our designers got frustrated," says Nagabhushan. "They were like, 'When is this going to stop?' And we said we are not going to stop making changes; we are not good enough yet. What happens is, you make a drawing change and it requires a tooling change. We were producing a new car every few months, if not in a few weeks.

There were issues with the team but our collective spirit was such that we could get over these bumps.

"Earlier, we were always working in specific functions. The designer would do his job and give it for prototyping. The testing guys would then get in and provide feedback, and it would go back to the design team. No professional likes somebody to come and tell him how to do his job. I will do my bit and you do yours — that's how it used to be.

"This is pretty much the case in most organisations even today. But I think the Nano has redefined, at least for Tata Motors, the relationship between designers and the testing people; the two functions actually became one and because of this we saved on time and resources."

Nagabhushan says the cost-quality-time challenge overrode all others in the engineering of the Nano. "We were squeezed from all three sides. And we started from scratch; that's never been done, because normally you begin from some kind of base and build a new product on that." Nagabhushan reckons the small-car team's ignorance of the magnitude of the challenges it faced was a boon. He compares this to the bumblebee, which succeeds in flying, despite being deemed incapable of it by the rules of aerodynamics, thanks to the power of its own ignorance.

RG Rajhans, a manager with the body systems engineering group that worked on the Nano, epitomises the collective spirit that Nagabhushan talks about. Rajhans and his team were responsible for the 'body' of the small car and its structure. The cost challenge was the toughest for these people and they tried every trick in the automobile manufacturing book, and a few from beyond, to stay inside the price barrier. That they had to opt for the conventional in the end may be considered a failure, but the successes they had were based in large part on what they had learned from the setbacks they suffered.

Cost was less of a concern than performance quality for Abhay Deshpande, who headed the vehicle integration team. He recalls 18 cross-functional teams working on the Nano, with solutions being decided in a manner that would not compromise the output of any one group. "This project was never about one designer or one team trying to solve a problem," he says. "We were all in it." The vehicle integration function, in particular, benefited from this approach, given the spread of its tentacles into all areas of the small car. "We were constantly trying to integrate two, maybe three functions into one: one wiper, a single casting for the engine, combination control switches and the like. Also, we were minimising the number of parts the car required, like we have three bolts, instead for four, for each tyre."

For safety systems expert Anil Kumar, the challenge was making the Nano match up to regulatory requirements, even exceed them, without compromising on passenger comfort. Cost, that constant bugbear, would come into play here too. Take the steering column. Most cars have collapsible steering columns, tested and proven many times over. The Nano does not. Instead, it has a system, anchored in the car's overall structure, that does as good a job as a collapsible steering column and at a much lower cost. "That's frugal engineering for you," says Kumar. "But there's more than cost reduction at work here. We took a fresh look at every fundamental engineering challenge."

A stiffer challenge was bringing the noise, vibration and harshness (NVH in automobile engineering parlance) quotient under control. The rear-engine placement meant the heart of the car was too close for comfort for those sitting in the back seat, and there was the noise to deal with. The Nano team struggled for two years with this twin problem. "We could have added more and more insulation material to reduce the heat, the vibration and the noise," says Wagh, "but that would have sent costing into a spin. So we changed the orientation of the cylinder head by 180° and we made a series of incremental improvements. The floor panel changed 10 times. The dashboard and seats, too, went through an equal number of modifications. It was painful. We were a long way into the project by the time we got what we wanted."

The point Wagh stresses here is that it wasn't any breakthrough solution that settled the issue. "If somebody comes and asks us what fantastic innovation solved the problem, I would have to say there was none. It was small, small things that different engineers did. We survived on this kind of perseverance and belief."

The fact that the Nano was never a fixed target, with all coordinates decided and every component nailed down, made the project team's task all the more difficult. Consider the issue of air conditioning. It was only in early 2007 that it was finalised that high-end models of the car would have it. Some team members thought this was not possible at that stage, given that it takes two years or more to get the air conditioning in place. Finding the right supplier was the big challenge and that was managed. "Such midcourse corrections were happening frequently," says Wagh. "Our initial thinking was premised on having a single model. But then we realised it did not make business sense; we had to have a platform with more than one option." So on came, along with the air conditioning, assisted brakes, high-end trims and the like.

The way the dashboard cluster and the wiper of the Nano were developed also illustrates the moving-target nature of the project. For the dashboard the team looked at different configurations, especially in the two-wheeler industry, for new ideas. The single-blade wiper had to undergo numerous modifications before it became acceptable. "The way it is parked is still not entirely satisfactory, but we are working on that," says Wagh. For the car's windows Ratan Tata had the team looking at airplane shutters as a solution. "We tried a lot of things in this area but we were not successful."

Ratan Tata's interventions and suggestions were a critical factor for the Nano team, particularly in understanding how customers would connect with the car. And there were others speaking up for the potential buyer, people like Vikram Sinha, then head of customer support at Tata Motors and a 33-year veteran with the company. Sinha and his team got involved in the Nano project in early 2007, forming a four-man cell and stationing it in Pune. These people, hardcore engineers themselves, would evaluate the prototypes now rolling out of the Engineering Research Centre and scrutinise them for reliability and ease of servicing. "The car had to be easy to service and simple to repair," says Sinha. "Our inputs were aimed at ensuring that."

In the beginning of 2008, the customer support team got to drive the finished product for the first time. They had mixed feelings. "We were excited about the appearance, the looks and everything, but there was some trepidation about the servicing of the vehicle, what with the engine in the rear and the tight space it sat in," says Sinha. "We did a lot of studies and brought in mechanics from our workshops. Our job was to make certain we had a car that was as good as it could get for customers."

Sinha and his team came up with 56 issues relating to the engineering of the car, including its pick-up, air conditioning and suspension. "We were perceived as people who pointed out problems, wet blankets and all that, but we took it in our stride," says Sinha. "Our objective always was that the customer should have the best, that the Nano should not be besmirched in any way."

Here was a man speaking from the experience of dealing with the Indica and the Tata Sierra, both of which had teething troubles. "I remember Tata Motors launching a truck in the early 1980s with a modern cab and amenities that are taken for granted today," recalls Sinha. "It drowned in the market because we did not take care of a variety of issues. We did not want that to happen with the Nano, especially so given all the attention focused on it. We have had customers telling us that journalists are calling them up asking if their Nanos are okay, whether they are having hassles with the car. There are people out there just waiting to pounce. We are under the scanner and we cannot afford to slip up."

With the troubles in Singur flaring up and other challenges mounting, the niggles with the Nano took time to resolve, but every one of them was addressed by Wagh and the project team. "From about November 2008 to the car's launch in March 2009, there was so much refining work done," says Sinha. "It's similar to when you are building a house. Putting up the structure is relatively simple; the finishing is what takes time. Same with a car; producing prototypes is easy, but finishing it, getting the right refinement, productivity and fuel efficiency — that's some undertaking."

The second, and probably more crucial, component of Sinha's engagement was what is known as the aftercare market, which means service centres and workshops that could keep the Nano in good shape after it hit the roads. "When we started planning our service network two years back, we wanted to have around 1,000 workshops by the time the car was launched," says Sinha. Tata Motors is short of its target by about 100 as of now, but even getting where it has — with some 900 workshops, each with four to five bays — was a huge effort. Some of these centres are franchisee arrangements with companies such as Exxon Mobil and TVS, but the vast majority have been set up directly by the company. It has involved training more than 2,000 people, at Pune and other places.

The fine-tuning of the Nano has not ceased even after its launch, with improvements being made to the car in a process that dates back to its unveiling at the Delhi Auto Expo. "In the long run, it will be the car's quality that counts," says Girish Wagh, "and the challenge we are facing here cannot be underestimated. After all, we are expecting to sell upwards of 350,000 units a year. That's about double the number being notched up by the largest-selling car in India at present. We can achieve that only by having extremely good quality and consistency, and improving these as we go along."

The improvements part had been imprinted on the small-car team, and was reiterated after a meeting Wagh had with Ratan Tata in February 2009. "He was driving the car and I was sitting behind him. I said I had some concerns and that if we told the team the product was fine, the effort to improve it would stop." Ratan Tata was in agreement with his project leader. Two months later, during a visit to the interim manufacturing facility for the Nano at Pantnagar in Uttaranchal, the chairman would come as close as he ever had to losing his cool with Wagh on the same point. "Mr Tata had wanted us to modify the side-view mirror and had told us so about a year earlier," says Mr Wagh. "We had delayed its implementation and here he was asking why. I started sweating, I was speechless. Then he calmed down and said, 'OK, we'll discuss this separately, we'll find a solution.'"

Finding solutions, of the marketing kind, has been the primary responsibility of S Krishnan, a senior executive with Tata Motors. In this matrix, getting dealers in place was top priority. Tata Motors had about 500 such outlets when the Nano was officially launched in March 2009 and it is aiming to increase that number to 800 by 2011. The complicated part here is to penetrate small-town and rural India. A second task on Krishnan's plate is outbound logistics, the price to be paid to reach the vehicle to a selling point. The cost of transporting a car is almost six times that of a two-wheeler.

"The two-wheeler price equation suggested we should be paying Rs2,200-2,300 to transport a Nano to a point of sale," explains Krishnan. "It was impossible to get to this target." The marketing team did the next best thing, working a minor miracle to bring the cost down to about twice what it takes to transport a two-wheeler. "We brought it down by more than 50 per cent from what it was earlier by assuring inbound logistics, or return loads, by carting more units onto the ferrying trucks and by partnering a single transporter. It becomes a logistical nightmare sometimes, but we have managed to cope."

The greater challenge will come when Tata Motors has to deliver tens of thousands of Nanos a month, and in making the customer's experience of visiting a showroom a pleasant one. "This experience is crucial because that's what will stay in mind in terms of the brand and the customer's association with it," says Krishnan. "Just because our customers are buying a less expensive car does not mean they have to be dealt with differently from somebody who's purchasing a costlier vehicle. Another challenge is educating customers on how to get the best out of their Nanos."

The manufacturing strategy for the Nano was primed for the customer's benefit. The distributed manufacturing idea was kept on the backburner, one that could be utilised as a parallel solution at a future date. This meant a return to the conventional concept of manufacturing the car at a single facility. Here is where Priyadarshan Kshirsagar, head of the manufacturing planning team, and his colleagues brought their expertise to bear. "From the beginning we had set a standard of operating three shifts over the 24-hour cycle," he says. "This demanded robustness in our internal processes, machine functioning, supply chain and logistics."

By August 2006 Kshirsagar and his team were ready to take the project into its execution phase. "We understood that the cost of the car was not just in the materials used but in our entire business process chain, and from a strategy perspective there was no confusion on manufacturing," he says. Synchronisation was a challenge, though, and bridges had to be built to connect support functions, vendor development, administration and the rest to the common goal of seeing the best possible product roll off the assembly line. "We made a lot of mistakes and we learned from them. We made sure we did not repeat them."

Installation and commissioning of the plant in Singur did not match expectations due to the challenges posed by the agitation and the need to raise the land at the project site following the flooding situation. The beneficial bit was that Kshirsagar and others were well prepared when they had to rebuild the plant in Sanand. As for the downside, horrid in every respect, Tata Motors was forced into doing what no other manufacturer, in automobiles or any other industry, ever had to: dismantle a brand new facility without producing anything at all and relocating lock, stock and barrel.

"No plant is ever designed for dismantling," says Kshirsagar, disillusionment crowding his face. "We had welded everything into place, fixed things to the ground expecting a long, long innings." The story of why that was not to be is sad and lamentable, and it is set in the confluence of politics and industry, conflicting ideas of development and the cussed realities of contemporary India.

Singur, a one-hour drive from Kolkata, is a peculiar amalgam of rural and urban, not big and brash enough to be called a city and too sprawling and busy to be tagged a town. Picking it as the site for the Nano plant was an option Ratan Tata had pushed for, but there was a load of searching and exploring done by the Tata Motors people before that came to pass. The scouting for a site had started as early as 2003, only to stall as other concerns emerged. It then began gathering pace in mid-2005 as various alternatives were considered.

The ideal site would have been somewhere close to Pune in Maharashtra, where Tata Motors had its main plant spread over some 900 acres of land. When that was ruled out, other automobile manufacturing hubs came into the picture: Chennai in Tamil Nadu, where Hyundai had its facilities, and Punjab and Uttaranchal in the north, where Maruti Suzuki had established its presence. The logic was that being close to a hub meant easy access to auto-component suppliers and proximity to big industrial centres. Dharwad in Karnataka and Uttarakhand, a state where Tata Motors already had a plant and where significant financial incentives were guaranteed, also got weighed up.

The Tata Motors team met government officials and ministers from different states and a recommendation was made at a meeting with Ratan Tata and Ravi Kant at Bombay House, the Tata headquarters, in January 2006. That's when Ratan Tata turned to Kant and asked him to look at West Bengal as a possible location, saying the chief minister and the Left Front-ruled government of the state were committed to bringing industry back to a region that had been left behind as big business flowed to other parts of India. The chairman was keen that Tata Motors take a lead in the reindustrialisation effort.

West Bengal became the chosen option for Girish Wagh and

his construction and manufacturing planning people from that point on, and it helped that the state government and its officials were more than forthcoming in welcoming the company to set up there. The Nano team visited eight sites across the state, four of them close to Kolkata, the state capital. What Tata Motors wanted was a continuous spread of about 1,000 acres, preferably close to Kolkata, and that's what they got at Singur. The site was fine, but other factors needed to be evaluated: financial benefits, getting suppliers in place, finding the right people. All of this happened in quick time and, in June 2006, the decision was finalised. Some six months later, Tata Motors got possession of the land.

Yet there were misgivings within the team about Singur from the beginning. "Many of us, internally, thought West Bengal may not be the right location, given its history of industrial disputes and the like," says Wagh. Ratan Tata, though, was certain. "He said it was a leap of faith, and that he believed the political leadership of the state was committed to the reindustrialisation cause. On the positive side, we knew that if we went our suppliers would follow and so would others." It seemed, at this stage, like a win-win-situation for all the players involved.

There were other positives too. The site was bang on a national highway — a substantial logistical benefit — and had an excellent frontage, an advantage because Tata Motors wanted to turn its plant into a state-of-the-art facility. However, in the rush to seal the deal, a critical concern was underestimated: the site sits in one of the lowest-lying regions of West Bengal, almost 16 feet below the road that ran in front of it.

MB Kulkarni, head of construction with the small-car project, and his people had studied the site area and past data to decide the amount of land filling required to be done to ensure that the plant would stay above the flood level. Murphy's Law was validated, though, when, in September 2007, unusually heavy rains left a portion of the facility under water. The Julkia river that flowed through a portion of the site burst its banks, the water-drainage mechanism for the plot had yet to be completed and, to make matters worse, some troublemakers opened a river gate that was meant to remain closed. A casual visitor would have been forgiven if he thought Tata Motors had set out to manufacture boats rather than cars.

"I was lost for words when I saw what had happened," says Wagh. "There were tears in my eyes. We had made a huge mistake in understanding what a worst-case flood scenario would be like; we never realised something like this could hurt us. The entire site was under water, boundary wall and all. It had become a big lake and people were moving around in canoes."

A review meeting was immediately scheduled with Ratan Tata. The chairman had never visited the site, but had pointed out its low-lying layout at a presentation much before the floods buried it. The team had responded that raising the height of the plant's shops would nullify the threat. Now a tense and jittery Wagh had, he thought, much to answer for. He need not have worried. Ratan Tata and Kant were sympathetic. "Let's find a way out of this," said the chairman.

Says Wagh: "After the meeting got over, I told Mr Tata, 'Sir, I was extremely strained coming into this meeting. I was worried about how you were going to take it.' He patted me on the back and said, 'Don't worry. Whatever has happened has happened. You have an action plan; now go ahead and implement it.' This, after we had lost time and money by ignoring a basic requirement. It was a tremendous gesture."

The challenge posed by the flooding would pale in comparison with the trouble that erupted as an agitation — powered by political ambition and fuelled by the disgruntlement of a small section of people who were unwilling to part with their land for the project — began to take hold. Tata Motors itself had never been part of the land-acquisition process; this was initiated and handled by the state government. What began as a loose and sporadic protest by a small number of local villagers was hijacked by outsiders with vested interests and malicious intent. Tata Motors would get dragged into a maelstrom it could never have anticipated or made allowance for.

Some of the project's spread was on rich farming land, and this added to the discomfiture of a state government that began to come under increasing pressure over the acquisition. Amarjit Singh Puri, a senior Tata Motors manager who was involved in finalising the Singur site, says the company never considered the political fallout of the acquisition process. "We looked at it from a purely business point of view. I still feel that if you take politics out of it, by and large people wanted the project to be completed."

Despite the agitation and the menace and ill-will it spewed, Tata Motors had from the start been working to establish a rapport with the community in and around the Singur site. Medical facilities were provided, computers and furniture given to schools and bore wells dug. More importantly, partnerships were forged with local non-government organisations and technical institutes to train people and enhance the skills base of the community. Even here, with activities so benign, it was far from smooth sailing.

"Our team had to constantly face protests from supporters of those opposing the project," says MB Paralkar, then head of corporate social responsibility at Tata Motors and a key figure in the events then unfolding. "The engagement of the people depended on their political alignment. Moreover, there was always a looming fear of violence. Our teams could move about only with police protection. Some of the beneficiaries of our initiatives — like the women from the self-help group we had formed to run a canteen at the site — were attacked, others were threatened. People were scared to be associated with us."

This was doubly unfortunate for the community at Singur, a place where poverty is stark and the basics of sanitation, health, and education mostly absent. "Initially the locals were uncertain about how to respond to us and some of them were upset about having lost their land," says Mr Wagh. "But gradually they got used to the idea of the plant and started seeing it as a livelihood source. We had a long-term plan for community welfare, but then things got bad and we had to stop our initiatives."

As the agitation gathered force, the threat of violence became ever present. There were some 400 people at the site from the early months of 2008, including foreign consultants, employees of the construction and technology partners and contractors. The pressure on these people, caught up in a situation they had no control over, worsened by the day. Tata Motors had its back to the wall. Something had to give, and it did. All work at the project site ceased on August 23, 2008. On October 3, at a press conference in Kolkata, Ratan Tata announced that Tata Motors would be leaving Singur. "This is a lonely decision," he said.

Giving up on Singur meant that the tremendous effort put in by Tata Motors in getting the facility up and running went waste. Finding the right people, blue collar and white collar, had been an especially tough task. The company had to spread the net wide to get qualified hands, particularly engineering talent. They did come eventually, some from as far as Chennai and Delhi, drawn by the innovative nature of the Nano programme and the opportunities it offered. "After the unveiling at Delhi we had people writing to us and asking about openings," says Girish Wagh. "We hired professionals from Toyota and Maruti, but filling the slots lower down was a tougher task."

Technical institutes in India churn out thousands of hopefuls every year. Getting them trained and ready for assembly-line functions is far from easy, though. Tata Motors addressed the problem by going local, selecting and training people, sending some of them to technical schools in Kolkata and others to its own facilities in Pune and Jamshedpur. These new inductees came back to Singur and were utilised when erection and commissioning work began at the site. The ripple effect of this was that vendors at various levels also started hiring locally. Further employment opportunities were generated by support services, in security, housekeeping and elsewhere. The sense of loss over the Singur pullout affected these people as much as anyone else.

Suppliers and vendors posed a different set of problems. Not all of them were convinced the Nano was for real till later in the day. Then, as the project progressed, they started jumping onto the bandwagon. There was a quickening in pace after a meeting in which Ravi Kant sent out a message to all vendors. "This project will happen, there is no doubt about that," he said. "Those who are uncertain can opt out now. Those who are interested, come on board."

The small-car team had always wanted to keep the number of parts suppliers as low as possible. "We did not want the figure to exceed 100," says BB Parekh, head of the sourcing group at Tata Motors. "We told our suppliers, 'Look, you need to stay with us, you need to share the risk of this project. We know there is going to be a ramp-up and a slow but accelerated growth. We don't know when we will reach the point when we start manufacturing a million Nanos a year. We think that will happen in five years, but we want the best possible price from day one, not when we reach the million figure."

Price aside, the biggest challenge on the supplier side was ensuring "quality robustness", as Prashant Saxena, Parekh's sourcing colleague, puts it. That's why a strategy of having, as far as was possible, only one vendor for any given component was pursued. "No vendor can be perfect, processes do fail," says Saxena, "which is why you have to keep chasing quality, auditing it, improving it. This is what makes the supplier's processes robust." The challenge that remains, adds Mr Saxena, is to bring rejections to a level of 200 ppm, or parts per million.

The Nano has about 2,000 parts — much fewer than a typical car like the Indica, for instance, which has around 3,000 — and up to 80 per cent of these parts are outsourced. Suppliers, thus, were vital to the success of the project. The vendor park that came up in Singur, and Sanand after that, was created to fulfil the outsourcing requirement in an innovative manner. "It is to the credit of our suppliers that they shared our vision," says Wagh. "Sure, we had plenty of convincing to do, but they came and started work, pouring in a lot of money. The Singur situation hurt them as much as it did us. It became a problem for us and our employees, for our suppliers and their employees."

The vendors and suppliers were a step behind Tata Motors as Singur was being set up. As things started unravelling, some of them hedged their bets. They decided they would have only the last mile of the value chain in Singur. The rest of their material would come from their own mother plant. If and when volumes picked up and the environment got stable, their involvement would deepen. Others, among them the sheet metal and plastic parts suppliers, had no choice but to invest at one go. These people would suffer as much as Tata Motors when the troubles broke out.

The Singur meltdown meant that Tata Motors had to get a fall-back facility ready in quick time to fulfil at least a part of the delivery commitment it had made to customers. There was not time for tears or remorse; the marketplace did not care. The decision was made to produce the first batch of Nanos from Pune and Pant-nagar. People were pulled in from Singur and sent to different locations to work on the project. "Everybody rallied to the cause," says Wagh. "We picked a leader for each task in the fallback plan. We set targets for what we could achieve over three months, six months, a year, a year-and-a-half."

The toll these efforts took on Tata Motors' people, psychologically as much as physically, is difficult to calculate. All the shifting and the moving affected employee families too. "We've had people migrating from many parts of India to join the Singur project, staying there for 12-18 months, settling down with family, getting school admissions and such — and then suddenly being told to move elsewhere," says Wagh. "Spouses had to find new jobs, then give them up. Kids had to change schools at a month's notice. It was a most difficult time. To this day we have employees in Pant-nagar or Pune with families in Kolkata or Ahmedabad."

Tata Motors has frequently been going beyond rules and regulations to support employees caught up in the storm caused by Singur, but there's only so much any company can do. "I feel sorry that we haven't done much for the families of our colleagues," says Wagh. "They had to undergo as much as any of us. Their contribution to the Nano has rarely been acknowledged."

"You may not believe this, but over the past four years no one that I know of working on the project has been home before 8-9 pm, at the earliest," says Atul K Vaidya, a member of the planning team. "This is the story of the whole team, not one or two people. We have built three factories in two-and-a-half years. Nothing like this has happened in the history of Tata Motors." Keeping motivation levels high in such circumstances can be an impossible task. To the credit of the Nano team, they learned to cope.

Tata Motors itself may have felt like a sacrificial victim among companies, nailed in its torment to the cross of unceasing misery.

Even before the Singur issue started derailing things, there were those who thought the Nano project would bomb, and within Tata Motors too. Doubters and naysayers are never in short supply with a programme such as this, where blind alleys and failure are frequent occurrences. Over time, the small-car team learned to live with this depressing irritant. "We had many people who thought the project was not possible," says Girish Wagh, a believer from before he was brought in to head the Nano team. "But our team was young and optimistic; we ignored the doubters and just went about our task, hoping and expecting that tomorrow was going to be better than today."

No amount of belief, though, could hide the damage caused by the Singur setback, and this affected other aspects of the project, primarily the engineering of the car. "We lost a lot of time because we were focused on Singur," says Wagh. "This is natural, probably. The entire company was kind of mentally drawn into it and this undermined our engineering preparedness on the product." The distractions were a dreadful drag at a time when Tata Motors had to redraw and recast its production plans. "We had to bring the project back on track, we had to find an alternate site for the main plant and we had to come up with a fallback arrangement."

In a trice, one project became three projects — from Singur to Sanand to the interim manufacturing at Pantnagar and Pune — and they had to be executed by the same team with the same number of people. Add to that the engineering changes taking place on the car and the refining of its design. "I am yet to visit all the locations where work on the car has been happening," says Wagh.

The top leadership, primarily Ratan Tata and Ravi Kant, were instrumental in keeping the team's spirit up even as the setbacks piled up. "Mr Tata was never discouraging in the face of our many failures," says Wagh. "He was tolerant of all the silly concepts we brought to him. I do not recollect a single incidence of him being irritated. He must have been, but he never showed it. His passion and enthusiasm rubbed off on everybody."

Failure was not a beast Wagh, a high achiever from his days as a student, had ever been familiar with. The Nano project changed that. "I used to find it difficult to handle or digest failure; there used to be a lot of mental friction," he says. "Then I realised it was not failure but aiming too low that was the crime. I learned from watching Mr Tata and Mr Kant, from other seniors and from my team. It was an education." Failure also taught Wagh and his team about humility. "Hierarchical power did not hold any value in this project. You have to convince people by other means. Mr Kant used to tell me, 'You have to sell your product concept to everybody.' This was a challenge and I've been doing it for a while".

Flexibility, openness, enthusiasm and the ability to enhance the skills of those around you — these were qualities Wagh sought when he put together the small-car group. What about technical capabilities? "A person designing a manufacturing process can refer to any number of knowledge data banks, but passion and emotional attachment cannot be accessed so easily." As with followers, so for the leaders on the project. Kant and Wagh led the way by keeping customer interest paramount, by trying to understand different points of view and ways of working, and never shying away from seeking help.

"There were three kinds of decisions we had to take: administrative, managerial and engineering," says Wagh. "Many engineering decisions come from knowledge and wisdom. I don't have that kind of knowledge or wisdom because I'm not from core engineering. That's where the guidance of Mr Akarte and Mr Telang proved critical. Young people, and the team was young, are prone to taking risks. Mr Akarte and Mr Telang kept us in control."

Wagh is too modest to mention it, but his own leadership was one reason the Nano project reached fruition the way it has. A second-generation Tata Motors man — his engineer father, Arun Wagh, retired from the company in 2001 after 35 years of service — Wagh joined the organisation as a trainee in 1992, did his engineering from the Maharashtra Institute of Technology before completing a post-graduate programme in manufacturing management from the SP Jain Institute of Management and Research in Mumbai. He rose up the ranks in quick time, being selected in the Tata executive selection scheme and become part of the Tata Business Excellence Model (TBEM) team.

Wagh may have been just another of the many outstanding engineers in Tata Motors but for the TBEM programme. That's when he came to the notice of Kant, who got him to head the development of the Ace small truck. The wide-ranging capabilities he displayed there brought him to the Nano project and the attention of the world outside Tata Motors. "I am grateful for the opportunities I have got in this company," he says. "I am lucky to have got the chance to work under the direct guidance of Mr Kant and the chairman, but there's nothing unique about what I have done. I have made sacrifices, especially on the family front, but so have countless others."

A shy and retiring person by nature, Wagh needed more than a bit of coaching when the media whirlwind hit him in the aftermath of the Nano's unveiling in January 2008. "I was extremely uncomfortable with the media, and I still am," he says. "The chairman decided to call me on to the stage [at the Delhi Auto Expo] and people started thinking I had a big role to play in this programme. It took a lot of effort to convince them that I was just one member of the team."

The attention frenzy kept building, though, and Wagh was hardly prepared for it. "I used to get requests from political parties wanting to felicitate me. I find felicitations disquieting in any case, and the political tinge made it worse. I kept declining them, saying I was in Singur or some such thing." This got particularly bad on one occasion, in February 2008, when Wagh went on a pilgrimage with his family. A temple functionary recognised me and made me jump the queue of devotees. I was so embarrassed. They kept calling me the Nano man." The embarrassment eased soon enough. "Fortunately, public memory is short. The euphoria subsided five-six months after the unveiling and everybody could get back to their jobs."

Far from reverence, it was respect that the small-car team felt for their project leader. "Girish has this ability to go to the heart of a problem," says Abhay Deshpande, the vehicle integration head. "He's not the type to sit in a cabin or instruct you on the phone. He will come to the shop floor, talk to you and make a decision. People are afraid of taking decisions. Not Girish; he is decisive." RG Rajhans, the body systems expert, praises another special quality Wagh has. "He brought us and whatever good work we were doing to the notice of Mr Tata and Mr Kant," he says. "He gave us visibility, allowed us to present our ideas to the bosses and highlighted our contribution. It made a big difference."

The opportunity to take chances and be creative was always there for the small-car team. The time and effort that went into exploring the plastics option epitomises this aspect of the development programme.

Plastic had been invented in the 1860s but its first application in automobiles happened only in the 1920s, and took a further 40 years for the material to be used widely in cars (the Citroen DS model of 1956 had a roof made of fibreglass reinforced with polyester). Since then plastic has challenged sheet metal as the base material for many automotive components. Lighter and stronger than sheet metal, non-corrosive and easier to mould, it affords greater flexibility in styling, building, the placing of components and in combining several parts into a single, integrated piece. For these reasons, and to get his engineers to try and breakthrough to another dimension on innovation, Ratan Tata wanted the small-car project to explore every opportunity on plastic as an alternative to sheet metal.

The way Ratan Tata saw the innovation equation in the project, Tata Motors may well have managed to make a vehicle like the Maruti-800 inside Rs100,000, but nothing extraordinary would have been achieved by that. It would have been just another cheap car. "That's not the purpose," he told BB Parekh, the sourcing chief at Tata Motors. "We need to bring innovation into it." Problem was — and remains — for all of its advantages, plastic is a lot costlier than sheet metal, but that was not going to constrain the chairman and his team as they set out, in early 2005, on a two-year journey to make plastic the calling card for their small car.

Plastic would lose out to sheet metal, finally, but not before more than 100 product prototypes had been developed and tested. Four factors were considered: direct material cost, ease of painting, manufacturing and servicing. The parts chosen were the four doors, bonnet, tailgate and fender (most modern car bumpers are already in plastic). Three supplier companies and seven plastic raw material manufacturers, among them General Electric, DuPont and Reliance, were sought out. General Electric went furthest in trying to help Tata Motors overcome conventional thinking and make the plastic experiment work, stationing three of its engineers in Pune for three months in mid-2005.

The pieces would not fall in place despite the best of efforts on both sides, mainly due to the cost factor. The cost threshold was Rs100-105 a kilo, the price for sheet metal that Tata Motors had arrived at. Try as it might, General Electric could not reduce the price of its engineered plastic below Rs140 per kilo, this after the company's chairman, Jeff Immelt, had met Ratan Tata in May 2006 and urged him to give his people another chance to crack the cost code.

Ratan Tata was most certainly disappointed that the Nano could not make extensive use of plastic components, but the endeavour had not been fruitless. The small car's engineers had learned plenty about the capabilities and limitations of plastic and, more importantly, the quest had resulted in the reduction of sheet-metal costs.

The space and opportunity to indulge in such an exploration had not always been available in Tata Motors, an organisation that for all its abilities, achievements and potential was also hidebound and compartmentalised in the way it functioned. This had already begun to change by the time Ravi Kant came to head it, but the new managing director would do more than anyone to guide and influence a true transformation in the company's outlook and in its operations. Kant revitalised Tata Motors by making it customer-oriented, getting employees to mix with and meet their colleagues at different company locations, and by eliminating the many barriers that had made teamwork difficult in previous years.

Kant started the process of identifying young talent and giving it a place at the top table. These high-potential people would often be part of informal lunch and dinner meetings organised by their affable managing director. The Nano project was full of people who had come through Kant's new system. Their extraordinary motivation level and capacity for work was the reason the project could be completed despite the numerous hurdles it encountered. The development programme gave birth to what is now called the Nano operating system, a production process that is still a work in progress but one that should come in handy as Tata Motors takes to the global motoring stage in future years.

The present, though, poses more pressing concerns, such as planning for a production target of rolling out one Nano every 53 seconds. "The challenges continue to fly at us from every dimension," says Kant. "We have to be relentless on keeping costs down, we have to be disciplined." It will take that and more if the vehicle is to live up to its promise. Credit-rating firm Crisil estimates that the Nano could on its own steam boost car sales in India by 20 per cent.

Tata Motors has invested so much in the Nano besides the Rs15 billion in financial resources allocated to the project thus far. And, while doing so, it has stayed true to the beliefs that characterise the Tata organisation. "We have fought against tremendous odds on so many fronts," says Kant. "And we have lived by our values from day one of this project. Our conscience is clear."

CHAPTER **3**

The cost frontier

Prices can be a pain in the wallet. For the development team working on the Nano project, they were a bee in the bonnet since the day Tata Motors chairman Ratan Tata let slip the Rs1-lakh price challenge for the small car at the Geneva Motor Show in 2003. From that point on, cost became the 'Big C' that had to be confronted and battled on a constant basis in a market-place where prices were as manageable as rush-hour traffic in Mumbai. Terms such as Gandhian engineering and frugal manu-facturing, which came to be associated with the Nano programme, were born of a cost calculus that seemed, at least in the beginning of the project, fantastical and set up for failure.

That the small-car team was able to roll out the Nano for the price the Tata Motors chairman had defined is an achievement that bids fair to count as a turning point in the history of automobile engineering, the latest marker in a timeline that started with Henry Ford and his mass production of the Model T and includes the European refinement of the motor car and the trailblazing Toyota production system, "the machine that changed the world". Yet, unlike the examples it shares space with in this pantheon, there is no path-breaking innovation for the Nano to boast of, only a relentless and near-fanatical focus by its development team on chipping away at the cost edifice it was faced with, component by component, process through process.

The Nano promises to herald a new method of mass motor car production, one aimed at developing countries, primarily India but also many others across the world, and less inclined to cater to the saturated markets of North America, western Europe and Japan. In this Nano methodology, a lower cost structure does not mean a reduction in the essentials of what goes into a car. Instead, it is about recasting the entire process of car manufacturing, including the development model, equation with suppliers, logistics, and sales and marketing. Most car companies develop a product and then put a price on it. Tata Motors did the opposite, but it had to play by conventional rules in other respects.

The determination to deliver a complete car rather than a barebones country cousin characterised the development of the small car. Cutting costs was all very well, but there was never any question of denying customers their due, be it on overall styling or engine performance, interior space or ride comfort, emission norms or safety. So how did the Nano team and the wider Tata Motors organisation pull off the minor miracle of creating a benchmark product while controlling costs to an extent that now seems extraordinary, especially when compared with the way automobiles are traditionally developed in the Western world? The answer lies in the details.

Take the Nano's electronic engine management system. The German companies Bosch and Siemens were in the running to supply the system, for which the Nano sourcing team had set a target price. This appeared ridiculously low when you consider that a similar system for the Indica, the hatchback from the Tata Motors stable, costs about twice that amount, but that was the nature of the pricing the team pushed for and, in most cases, secured. "We selected Bosch to supply the system and we got them to do 90 per cent of the development work for it," says BB Parekh, head of sourcing in the Nano programme. This was typical of how the development effort on components was shared in the project, with suppliers betting on the Nano in as significant a measure as Tata Motors.

The engine management system comprises 13 parts. Bosch created a stripped-down version of its standard system, with a reduced number of components and sensors. The sourcing people wanted Bosch to quote a price for each of the system's parts, just so they could release the purchase orders for them. The Germans were flummoxed. "They told us they didn't know how to get down to the figure we wanted," says Parekh, "and no clue about what individual elements of the system would cost. They said, 'We have committed to your price and that's what we will give it to you for.' This happened before the Singur crisis erupted and Bosch has had to, like many other suppliers, put their investment plans on hold, but they have continued to hold onto this price."

A factor in Bosch's belief in the Nano project has been the personal friendship Ratan Tata has with Bernd Bohr, chief of the German company's automotive business. On a visit to India in early 2009, Bohr met Ratan Tata and Ravi Kant, the former managing director of Tata Motors and currently the company's vice chairman. He assured them of Bosch's support and commitment to the project. "We understand the problems you are facing," he said. "We are facing bigger problems but we will manage. Let's get to 2011-12; we will come and see where we have reached and then we will talk about it. As of now, I'm taking this as a business risk."

Suppliers were, from the start of the Nano project, factored in as critical to its success. About 80 per cent of the 2,000-odd components in the small car comes from component vendors. The idea was to limit the number of suppliers to about 100 and there was a cost-savings logic to it. "The way we saw it, to hit the lowest possible cost we had to guarantee maximum business volume to our suppliers," explains Parekh. The single-supplier strategy that Tata Motors pursued with vigour has played a vital part here. The idea was to forge the strongest possible partnership with vendors and to cultivate a truer sense of sharing, of business risk as much as with long-term profitability, and of stability in relationships. A single supplier for any given part would, obviously, get the greater benefit than if two or three were in the fray. "We tried to identify suppliers with the best of capabilities and resources. We were planning for up to 1 million units a year. We needed people who could generate such numbers."

Tata Motors was also banking on getting on board suppliers who could secure cost reductions by way of concept, in design as well as manufacturing. "That's why we were looking for suppliers with design capabilities," says Parekh. "We wanted them to contribute to product design rather than depend on our designers to draw the final line on anything and everything." Most importantly, the sourcing team wanted component manufacturers who would give it the best possible price from day one of the project, rather than after production hit a peak, as is the general rule in manufacturing. "We didn't have the option of beginning with a high cost and then gradually bringing it down."

Going unconventional wherever possible was another way of licking the cost problem. Nowhere did this aspect come into play as much as it did with the seats for the small car, to the extent that the development team was at one point poring through furniture catalogues. Even that did not provide a solution to what was turning out to be a particularly sticky issue.

The target cost set by the team for a seating arrangement that would accommodate five people was much lower than anything available in the market. Finally, though, the team found the seating system it was looking for from Tata Johnson Controls, a joint venture company of Tata AutoComp Systems. "Those were breakthrough prices," says Parekh. "It shows the kind of cost level we have achieved."

The supplier-side story here has a distinctive script, with a plot in which long-term partnerships involving Tata Motors and auto component manufacturers underpinned the wresting of substantial cost benefits. "We got our suppliers excited as the project progressed, and we got the lowest possible development cost on components," says Parekh. "Our suppliers have borne quite a bit of risk on the Nano." This did not happen without effort. Tata Motors exerted a lot in selling the concept of the small car to suppliers unfamiliar with a project quite unlike anything they had been associated with previously.

Innovation in design and the prospects of long-term advantages were what pulled suppliers into the project, not flea-market bargaining or arm-twisting on cost. "At day's end you must make sure that whoever the supplier and whatever the price he is offering, there has to be a strong business case," says Parekh. "He must profit from the project; only then will he support you. Otherwise you get a price that is not viable and a supplier who will go bankrupt trying to keep up."

The Nano experience with suppliers was far removed from what Parekh had seen while working on sourcing for the Indica project, and it highlighted the distance Tata Motors had covered since getting into motor car manufacturing back in 1998. "I remember the scepticism of some suppliers during the Indica project, their telling us why we could not pull it off and asking why they should invest money in an unproven venture. There was no such credibility issue with the Nano, and one big reason was Mr Tata talking about it so much. His sincerity provided the boost we needed to sell the Nano idea to our suppliers."

Ratan Tata may have made the Rs1-lakh commitment, but cost was never the overriding consideration for the chairman. "The customer was paramount in his line of thinking," says Parekh. "He did not hand down directives; his way was to try and convince people. He kept telling us to look at our costing concept and make the car better. We would have one meeting, a second meeting and then a third and finally people just accepted his point of view. He never gave up. He never compromised."

The learning on cost that Tata Motors has got thanks to the Nano project has been, simply put, priceless. "What it has done is show us that anything's possible," says Parekh. "We are not going to get daunted by cost targets now. We have come to understand that by working in the right manner along with suppliers we can have the cost we want without cutting corners on deliverables. We have, I think, found a way to secure cost-effective, as opposed to cheap, solutions."

There are numerous factors that have allowed the Nano to stay ahead of the cost curve. Its dashboard is a large single piece of plastic and, with its central placing, designed for right- as well as left-hand-drive markets. Instrumentation is basic in this centre console and there is a caved-in space for storage on the front-passenger side. The base model of the car has just one control stalk on its steering column for lights, signals and wiper (higher-end versions have two). The steering rack itself is a single-piece steel tube, which drastically reduced machining and assembly cost.

The basic Nano does not have storage pockets in its doors (high-end Nanos do). It has a simple door panel, its bumpers are made of plastic (and not painted in the base model) and there are air scoops on both sides of the car, one that carries air into the engine and the other to cool it. The car's seats are fixed to a steel bar that runs across its cabin, providing a safety anchor and some degree of side-impact protection. The hatchback option was discarded to save on cost and weight. This has resulted in the baggage space being under the rear seat, accessed by folding the seat forward.

The rear-engine placement has yielded dividends on costs as has the car tyres using three nuts. The side mirror is there only on the driver's side in the standard configuration, there is no slot to fill fuel (this is under the hood), and the car makes do with a single windshield wiper. The body of the Nano is light in weight (another cost-reduction advantage) and its wheels are smaller than is the norm with cars, and their sizes in the front and back differ (to improve performance and ride quality, and to better balance a car that is heavy at the rear due to the positioning of its engine). And there's the compact dimension of the car (the smaller the vehicle, the lower the cost of constructing it). Cost was the reason the Nano development team had to give up on its long-drawn quest to use plastics and adhesives instead of welded steel.

Vivek Sahasrabuddhey, a member of new product introduction team on the Nano project, talks about the cost-reduction exercise as driven, to a large extent, by design. "In a traditional design you have a traditional cost. We had to go beyond the traditional to meet our target," he says. "So we looked at integrating functions, at combination switches and the like. We tried to minimise the number of parts needed. We conducted workshops with suppliers. We kept track of costs at every turn."

Automobile industry experts say the secret behind the low cost of the Nano is a concept called target pricing (also known as target costing), a process that determines what features and functions are essential from a customer's perspective. For instance, do customers want two or four doors? What should the engine capacity be? Should the windshield wipers have two blades or one? Once the features and functions are finalised, target costs are assigned to each component or system, to every nut and bolt. That's why the Nano has a variable transmission instead of gears and an instrument cluster without anti-glare coating or screws.

The target pricing concept also defines the supply chain process. Cost and waste are driven down by reducing inventory, eliminating waiting times and delays, increasing the utilisation of warehouses and trucks, finding the best sites for warehouses and plants, and zeroing in on an optimum transportation network. These efforts have, additionally, minimised the working capital cost on the small car.

Target costing of a different kind is also evident in the price of the Nano, from the base model of which Tata Motors expects little profit. Profits, the company reckons, will accrue from the higher-end models, which have air conditioning, electric windows, colour-coded bumpers and a host of other features. (To see how the Nano compares with a 'low-cost car' from the developed world, you have to place it alongside the two-seat Smart Fortwo, which sports a price tag that is four-five times higher.)

"We wanted to shock the customer, in the sense of giving him much more than what Rs1 lakh could reasonably buy," says Prashant Saxena, Parekh's colleague on the sourcing team. "Costing is a reality, you cannot wish it away. Pricing may be policy, but costing is a fact. We had a target cost. We broke this down and cascaded it to every component." There was more to it. As Priyadarshan Kshirsagar, head of the manufacturing planning function in the project, remembers it, the development team had to first believe the Nano's seemingly impossible cost equation could be realised. "Frankly, back in 2006 when I got into the project, hardly anybody thought we could control the car's cost," he says. "This was the company's little secret project. It was only after working on it for a long time, day by day, that we came to be convinced this was indeed possible."

For the manufacturing planning team, charged with the responsibility of getting the right technology and equipment in place for mass production of the Nano, the cost challenge took a different trajectory. "Much of what we are using at our plant is also used by manufacturers such as Mercedes and BMW," says Kshirsagar, head of the manufacturing planning team. "What we have done is remove all the frills and all the excess automation. We have taken exactly what we want and we have aggressively chased the costing we wanted. There are cases where our suppliers have asked us not to reveal the prices we have got for their equipment and technology."

Looking back, facing and overcoming the cost challenge may appear less daunting than it actually was for the Nano project team. "We had to go through more than 8,000 ideas, bound together through three waves of cost-reduction initiatives, to reach where we have," says Girish Wagh. "Everything associated with the word 'cost' was looked at." This meant direct material cost and variable and fixed conversion cost; supply chain and logistics; inspection and warranty; financing and working capital management; and taxation, interest and depreciation.

Early and intense engagement with vendors was the way costs were controlled. "Cost reduction ideas were generated with the entire prospective vendor base and not just selected suppliers," says Wagh. "In addition, the entire vendor base was integrated through information technology to have 'just-in-sequence' supplies, and this helped reduce inventories. In the third wave of our cost-minimisation exercise, we revisited what we had achieved in the first and second waves. All said and done, we got to where we wanted without ever compromising on vehicle performance."

The cost factor could have ended up being an albatross around the Nano development team's neck were it not for the level-headed manner in which the impediments arising from it were handled by Ravi Kant and Girish Wagh, the two leaders of the project. "I used to tell the team not to bother too much about cost," says Wagh, "that the critical part was solving whatever engineering problems we faced and then addressing the cost issue. I didn't want people to get bogged down and defensive about things."

Keeping up with and working on the suggestions Ratan Tata had whenever he visited Pune to review the project's progress was another matter. The chairman took a particularly keen interest in the car's styling, and his promptings tended to get Wagh and his boys worried because they inevitably meant an increase in cost. This was par for the course in a development programme where every penny counted, but that did not make it any easier for the

Nano team. It got to a stage where Kant had to intervene. He pulled aside Wagh one day and said, "Don't get stuck on one rupee and five rupees and ten rupees. Execute whatever he wants on styling and we will see how to compensate on the cost elsewhere."

Ratan Tata himself was acutely aware of the cost pressures on the team. Ideas from his end usually came with a question: "Girish, I know you will say this is going to increase costs, but can you do it nevertheless?" Wagh was never in doubt. "I would say, 'Sir, you tell us what you want and we'll take care of the cost.' My team did not always take kindly to me saying such things. The way they figured it, this did not help them keep costs in check. To me, though, it was clear that Mr Tata's forward-thinking suggestions had to be accommodated; that's what the customer would want and no one understood the customer better than the chairman. We had to banish this image that Tata cars had of not being good enough in their initial run."

A far greater challenge was controlling cost at a time when the prices of commodities and raw material were going through the roof, especially during the four-five years leading up to the Nano's launch in 2009. "To add to the troubles, some of our cost targets were not well-defined," says Wagh. "This was due to the evolutionary process through which the design and development of the Nano happened, and there was nothing we could do about that. We had a lot of iterations — at the layout level, the aggregate level, with subsystems and components — to see how best we could cut costs." How much was all this worth? "I reckon our efforts brought overall costs down by 25-30 per cent."

There was no breakthrough innovation that made this cost saving a reality. Rather, it was a series of minute improvements even engineering boffins might labour to find interesting that did the job. "We finally found a solution that may not have achieved our objective to the fullest extent, but we got one that was acceptable," says Wagh. Judging from the reaction of the automobile world and the layperson to the Nano, the solution seems more than acceptable, yet there were never any guarantees that the customer would play along. "The customer still thinks he should get for Rs100,000 what others are getting for five times as much," says Kant. "It's like expecting to buy a three-bedroom apartment in an upscale locality for the price of a two-room pad in the suburbs." On the bright side, that is a compliment to Tata Motors and what Indians insist that the Nano be.

Prakash Telang, Tata Motors' managing director for India operations, thinks the focus on customer expectation helped the small-car project in more ways than one. "We counted every rupee to reduce costs," he says. "At the same time, we did not want to take away anything at all from customers. We were always conscious that they should not say the Nano is some cheap box they are getting into." Telang, a tall man, had a role to play in ensuring that would not happen, even if only as a passenger. He and Ratan Tata, almost as tall, would place themselves inside the car on most of its important testing runs. "Mr Tata would be in the front seat and I would sit behind him. We were comfortable enough. This spaciousness on the inside surprised people."

The roominess of the Nano on the inside is in sharp contrast to the compact look it has from the outside. The car's design is what makes the difference stand out. Nikhil Jadhav, a member of the Nano's design team, reckons the absence of a watertight cap on design costs afforded the people working on it a free hand. "Typically, design is always looked upon as a costly affair, something that always adds to a car's price," he explains. "This wasn't how we saw it with the Nano. We never lost elements of design and the tricky bit was that this is not a simple design."

Wagh credits the sourcing team with making a vital contribution in the battle against costs, not just on the car's components but also on machinery and equipment for manufacturing the Nano. He's not so kind on the subject of the forced pullout from Singur, which skewed all cost calculations and, for a while, threatened to derail the project. In the circumstances, to stick by the original price tag for the Nano was courageous. It was a leap of faith, a display of conviction and certitude that had Ratan Tata's signature all over it.

The chairman had been in Pune all of the week prior to the Nano's unveiling at the Delhi Auto Expo in January 2008, going over preparations and making sure there would be no glitches. Wagh was with Ratan Tata and he was still not sure if his boss intended to hold on to the price. "One evening I asked him if he was going to declare the price at the unveiling. He didn't say anything, so I started talking to him about the changes that were happening in commodity prices, the unknowns and the like. I asked him if we could delay the pricing decision till when the car was officially launched. Again, he didn't say anything."

Ratan Tata may not have responded to his team leader's questions, but his mind was made up by then. "A promise is a promise," said the Tata Motors chairman and inspiration-in-chief behind the Nano as he showcased his baby to the world. The price would be what he had said it might be five years, and a million struggles, before his dream found its place in the motoring sun.

CHAPTER **4**

From Singur to Sanand

A tul K Vaidya had come to take one last look at a dream he knew would soon go sour, and he was reduced to tears. A senior engineer with the planning team on the Nano development programme, Vaidya had wangled a visit to Singur, the original site for the small-car plant, because he was in on a secret only a handful of others were aware of, that Tata Motors may have to close down its soon-to-be-completed Nano facility and move out of volatile West Bengal. Now here he was, on a searingly hot September day in 2008, a week before the closure would be announced to a disbelieving world, in a giant industrial shed with thousands of tonnes of idle machinery, and he could not help but cry.

"We had started from scratch with the plant, we had put in so many months of hard work," he says. "The investment, the manpower, the enthusiasm, the effort — all wasted. It was too much to take." Accompanying Vaidya on this farewell tour of remembrance was a security official and his planning team colleague, Jaydeep Desai, neither of whom had any inkling of what was to come a few days hence. "Jaydeep was baffled. He kept asking me what was wrong, why I was getting emotional. I couldn't tell him what I knew. This week you are rearing and ready to manufacture a pathbreaking product, the next week you begin to pack up and leave. It was so painful."

There was plenty of pain for everyone at Tata Motors, and a lot many people outside the company, to share as the reality of the Singur pullout began to sink in. This was not how it was meant to be. The decision to choose the site, prompted by chairman Ratan Tata, had been made after various options had been considered, a few of them in West Bengal itself.

Negotiating terms for the deal on behalf of Tata Motors were senior executives Amarjit Singh Puri and RS Thakur. An initial agreement was signed with the West Bengal government in late March 2006. This happened on a day of some attrition, and the setting for the sealing of the deal was a bed in a Kolkata hospital. Thakur, one of the authorised signatories for Tata Motors, had injured his shoulder in a car accident en route from Jamshedpur to Kolkata. Puri, the other authorised signatory, was being pursued by the West Bengal media, a bunch whose persistence while chasing a story is, as Tata Motors officials would discover in the coming days, on par with Hollywood paparazzi. "I was in a taxi and these guys were hounding me," recalls Puri. "I was moving around the city in this taxi from 11am to 2pm and I finally managed to shake them off. Thakur could not get off his bed so I went to the hospital and got his sign."

That probably was a portent of how things would unfold as the Singur issue came to a boil, fuelled by an incendiary mix of partisan politics, fiercely competing ideas of industrial development and local disgruntlement with the state government's land-acquisition process. That all wasn't well on the ground was evident to Tata Motors officials right from the time, back in January 2007, when the foundation stone for the facility was laid in a function that was deliberately kept low key. Police personnel were present even then and they would soon become a permanent part of the landscape, a continuing and constant reminder of the threat the project faced.

"We had put up a preliminary kind of fencing around the site, but there were people breaking through and causing trouble," says Dilip Sengupta, a senior Tata Motors executive deputed to mediate with government functionaries and officials of the district administration. "We then started constructing a proper boundary wall and we did this in quick time, completing about 14km of it in 45 days." The wall was meant mostly to demarcate the site rather than keep people out. This was in keeping with Ratan Tata's view that the facility needed to be showcased to the world, not turned into a prison that locked Tata Motors workers in.

All the fencing in the world could not prevent flooding caused by rains in a low-lying property prone to water logging. This was an aspect that was underestimated by the planning and construction team and it would come back to haunt the project. The first of the flooding disruptions happened in August 2007, and the elements were not entirely to blame. A group of villagers, Tata Motors officials later realised, had dug small canals on the periphery of the property. Water gushed through and made a hassle created by nature a full-blown problem. A second flooding incident followed close behind, but this and the earlier one were dwarfed by an unusually heavy spell of rain in September-October that left the project in deep trouble.

The floods and the remedial measures that had to be undertaken to resolve matters — raising the level of the shops, getting proper water drainage systems in place, relaying 5,000 square metres of flooring, etc. — cost the small-car team plenty of money and four months in lost time, not to mention the heartburn and frustration caused by consequent delays. There were lessons to be learned from the flooding setback and lapses to be acknowledged. No one was more forthcoming on this front than Girish Wagh, the leader of the small-car team. There was no going back now and the resilience of spirit that characterised the entire Nano project came to the fore, yet already the feeling was gaining ground that setting up in Singur was anything but straightforward.

Tata Motors was always keen to make the Singur facility an advertisement for its competence and capabilities, its values and way of functioning. As Debasis Ray, the company's head of corporate communications, saw it, people in West Bengal, government officials as well as media, needed to have first-hand experience of what Tata Motors stood for and how it ran plant operations elsewhere in India. Visits to the company's Pune plant — a remarkable facility extending to about 900 acres of land — were organised for members of the West Bengal government's committee on industry and commerce and for the media.

"We wanted to show them how an automobile plant functions, the scale of our operations and what we as a company do in and around these operations," says Ray. "One of the journalists was particularly impressed with what he had seen, especially our community development initiatives, and the word he used to describe how he felt was *mantramoogdha*, which means spellbound in Bengali." But the spell did not extend to Mamata Banerjee, currently India's minister for railways and back then, in early 2007, the head of the Trinamool Congress.

In Singur and its surrounding areas, the Trinamool Congress has a prominent presence, yet the majority of locals whose land had been acquired for the Nano project were supportive of what Tata Motors had set out to accomplish. There was, however, an undercurrent of discontent with the manner in which land had been taken possession of in Singur.

Construction work at the site started in February 2007. So too did the protests, scattered, irregular and feeble at first, but gathering in menace and momentum almost in step with the project's progress. There was a muscular police presence even then, with up to 800 personnel. The number increased to more than 1,200 in the days ahead, and there were some 350 locally hired security hands for night patrolling. This sort of strength may ordinarily have been more than enough deterrence to keep troublemakers at bay and secure the property, but Singur was no ordinary case and those leading the protest against the project had decided early on to make violence and the threat of it their weapons of choice.

On March 12, 2007, the police diffused crude bombs and landmines placed near the boundary wall of the site. Worse happened a week later, when bomb explosions along the periphery of the facility caused panic among construction workers. This was followed by an incident in which 20-25 agitators breached the compound wall and burned construction machinery. There would be no letup as the protesters got more brazen and vicious. Labourers at the site were threatened, many were beaten up and others told to leave. A security post was set on fire in December 2007. Dumpers were destroyed and rampant theft, of building material, steel, cables and machine parts, became everyday occurrences.

It was, however, the danger to life and limb that caused the deepest worry. In July 2006, Amarjit Singh Puri, Tata Motors' liaison person with the state government, got a taste of how bad things could get when a mob of agitators besieged the car he was travelling in. "I was inside the site with these Canadian architect consultants and a colleague, showing them the layout and stuff," says Puri. "Suddenly a mob surrounded us. They started banging on the car, telling us to go back to where we had come from and shouting that we could never have the land. There were 300 of them and we were scared out of our wits. I got the Canadians back into the car and then my colleague and I got in. We attempted to move out but that was impossible. They were pounding on the windows, the bonnet, and the trunk. I had to do something, so I called the [the West Bengal government's] secretary for industry. He said he would send the police to get us out. Meanwhile, I tried talking to the protestors. They were in no mood to listen. They kept hollering till the police came and rescued us. It was a chilling experience."

It was not as if all of Singur was ranged against Tata Motors. Puri and those in the car with him visited the block development office later that day and were welcomed by people with bouquets, saying the arrival of the Tatas in Singur would change the region for the better. "But we did not know what the real situation was inside the villages. And then this mob episode happened. It opened our eyes. I mean, we expected a friendly and congenial environment to work in. We did not want to be in a place where we had to be escorted by police everywhere we went. I once walked into Singur unaided and unannounced and the police chief gave me a mouthful. It was like I had made a mistake and I had to be apologetic and say sorry. You feel, what the hell, what's going on here."

Between March 2007 and August 2008, the protesters forcibly

enforced 12 *bandhs* (the Hindi word for general strikes) in Singur. An engineer employed with Shapoorji Pallonji and Co, the infrastructure developers for the facility, was assaulted and workers at the site were being continually threatened with violence if they did not leave. Many fled and Tata Motors and its contractors started finding it impossible to get replacements. As if all this wasn't bad enough, trouble erupted on other fronts: some settlements inside the site were proving difficult to be relocated, a syndicate supplying material for the project started creating problems, and prefabricated structures for the facility's paint and press shops got held up due to delays in processing by the customs people.

Though it did not seem so at the time, the point of no return was probably reached when, in February 2008, some of the protestors were beaten up by the police after a spike in the agitation. Banerjee and some of her supporters were arrested and this sparked a fresh wave of disturbances. It added to the anger already hanging heavy in the West Bengal air following a far worse exhibition of the state's harshness, when 14 people protesting against a proposed special economic zone in faraway Nandigram, a rural area in Midnapore district, were killed in firing by police forces.

Girish Wagh, a taciturn person in settled settings, gets worked up still when he casts his mind back to those tumultuous times. "The villagers had, I believe, come around to accepting that the plant would come up," he says. "But the situation changed after that February uproar." Wagh, his team members and everyone else associated with the project could now move around only with police protection. "It was so far removed from normal, the threats, the assaults and everything. We could not function."

To an outsider it can appear astonishing that despite all these troubles the Nano development team was on its way to getting the Singur facility ready for production by July 2008. But they had not reckoned with Banerjee's resolve, and her resources, to stretch the issue to a calamitous conclusion. In August 2008 she played what would be her final hand, launching a *dharna* (sit-down protest) in which instigation and provocation of the police and other arms of the state administration were constantly-used tactics. The police, chastened by Nandigram and the February incident, were soft targets and the agitators became even more emboldened.

"Our people, our contractors, our vendors — everybody was on edge," says Wagh. "I would spend the first two hours of any given day listening to contract labourers who had been threatened or beaten up. Work was suffering and, meanwhile, I had these local ruling party leaders asking me not to worry, saying they would provide replacement labour for those who were leaving. I kept telling everyone we were not doing anything wrong, that the difficulties and the agitation would pass, that once the plant came up the benefits to Singur and the entire region would be there for all to see. That's how we kept our morale high, or people would have broken down."

Mamata Banerjee had been approached to sit across the table and work out a solution, but that was not to be. The August *dharna*, which saw the protestors blocking the national highway in front of the Singur facility and barring anyone from using the approach roads to the plant, brought matters to a head. Arrangements to stay back at the site were rudimentary. This meant that people had to continue coming in from wherever they were being put. With the main gates of the facility shut and the usual approach roads to them being barricaded by the protestors, those commuting to the plant — among them Tata Motors employees, contractors, suppliers, foreign consultants and labourers — had to run a gauntlet every day to get to work.

These people had to use a circuitous route that involved five hours of travel one way, move in convoys with police protection, and stay on guard at all times. "Some of these guys could get to their places of accommodation only by 2am at night, and they had to set out again at 7am the next morning," says Wagh. The roundabout travel route, too, came to be blocked when the agitators got wind of it, and they had a television channel to thank for the information.

A reporter and cameraperson got into one of the 50-odd vehicles making the daily trip and they put a spin on the story about the sacrifices and struggles Tata Motors and its people were undergoing to turn Ratan Tata's dream project into reality. "I think this further infuriated the protestors," says Wagh. "That evening a mob of protestors stopped the first batch of our vehicles as they were beginning to leave the plant through the only gate open to us. One of the vehicles managed to get through, but three others were stuck." The protestors started banging the sides of the vehicles with stones and then they clambered on board. They started falling at the feet of those inside and pleading with them not to come to the site from the next day. The Tata Motors people were terrified.

"I was in one of the shops and I got a call about the situation at the gate with the vehicles," recalls Wagh. "A colleague said he would go and see what the problem was. He went to the gate and was overwhelmed by what he encountered. He called me up and said, 'Girish, this is serious,' and he gave the phone to a young engineer who had to face the mob. The boy broke down. 'What have we done to deserve this,' he asked me." Something snapped inside Wagh, a team leader who had seen his people and his project suffering way too much strife for scant reward in an environment polluted by the politics of opportunism and the hostility this bred.

"I went to the gate and spoke to the police officials and others present there," says Wagh. "We negotiated for more than two hours. The demonstrators were unrelenting and the police were disinclined to use force, and rightly so given the charged atmosphere. Then it started raining quite heavily and the protesters moved away looking for shelter. The police called us and said this was the chance for our cars and buses to leave. That's what we were doing when a Japanese national, one of about 35 foreign nationals who were employed with the different consultants helping us, became agitated, shall we say. "I don't want your car,' he started shouting. 'I don't want Tata Motors. I'll go walking.' It was scary."

The *dharna* had begun on August 18, a Monday, and this was Friday night. "I decided then that we would stop coming to work from Saturday, August 23; we couldn't continue in those circumstances," says Wagh. "I called Ravi Kant [then the managing director of Tata Motors] and told him of our decision. He was more than supportive, saying he would back us all the way." Ten days earlier Wagh had met Ratan Tata in Pune. The chairman had made it clear that the safety and well-being of his people were paramount. Now the die was cast; there could be no going back.

The question that cropped up was how to keep everybody engaged when the site was out of bounds. "It had started giving us sleepless nights," says Wagh. "We had built our team after a great amount of effort and we didn't want to lose people, but credit to all the team members, they continued to work from their hotel rooms and guest houses. I would be moving from one place to another, meeting them, coordinating and trying to get done whatever work was possible." This unwieldy state of affairs continued for the next six-seven weeks, even as behind-the-scenes endeavours got underway to salvage the situation.

There would be no solution, far less salvation, for Tata Motors. "We stopped work at the plant on August 23 and we kept waiting till October, hoping things would improve," says Wagh. They did not, and not for lack of effort on the company's part. The politics of West Bengal would not allow it. "Any dissection of the Singur imbroglio cannot get completed without an understanding of the politics behind it," explains Sunirmal Patra, a retired lieutenant colonel with the army who had the onerous task of handling security and administrative affairs for Tata Motors at the site. "Protestors were methodically mobilised from all over the state. There was a negligible number of locals; people were brought in from outside. The logistics and planning were so good."

Patra was another of those who came face-to-face with the fierceness of the agitators. This happened in January 2008 after 139 men hired by the state administration to provide additional security at the site were relieved of their responsibilities. These people were communist supporters and did not take kindly to the decision. "They had gathered inside the facility and a situation was developing," says Patra. "A security colleague and I went to see what was happening. There were about 40 of them. They had iron rods, sticks and crude bombs, the kind that make a noise rather than do much damage. They charged towards us. The first instinct was to run, but I stood my ground; maybe it was the army training that kicked in. We got talking to them, reasoned with them and the rods and sticks were lowered. It was a close thing."

This was no isolated incident. Manual labourers and other construction workers had to bear the brunt of the menace unleashed by the protestors. "Most of these workers have, at some time or the other, been threatened or assaulted," says Patra. "They had to commute by the local train coming into Singur and there was no way they could avoid the agitators. They even had crude bombs being thrown into the houses where they lived." The Nano Bachao Committee, a locally organised group backing the project, suffered worse. "There was a clash between the committee people and the protestors and that was the end of the committee. The protestors had all kinds of weapons. One man had his leg broken, others were merely bloodied."

Patra still believes the majority of locals were in favour of the project. "We had villagers saying they did not comprehend why or how Tata Motors would consider pulling out. There was this feeling, more out of hope than anything concrete, that the Tatas had some sort of alternate plan to get the factory going. Of course, we did not. It was a game of politics and it resulted in an ideal project turning into a lose-lose situation for everybody involved."

Speaking in an interview on a television news channel back in December 2006, Ratan Tata had hinted at there being more than politics behind the attempts to derail the Singur project. "It is not just political, because I happen to know that some of our competitors are also fuelling some of this fire; they would be very happy if the project got delayed," he said. "If I believe that we were doing something wrong, then I will be the first one to pull out. If I believe that this is being manipulated and turned around to meet some specious cause, then, I think, what I would do is dig my heels in... You put a gun to my head and pull the trigger or take the gun away. I won't move my head."

But there was only so much the Tata Motors chairman, a person of steely resolve, could take. On a rainy evening on October 3, 2008, Ratan Tata announced at a hurriedly organised press conference in Kolkata that the Nano project would be shifted out of Singur and West Bengal. For Debasis Ray, the corporate communications head, that day remains etched in memory. "The journalists present were mostly dyed-in-the-wool types, and I saw a few red-eyed people there."

Earlier that day, Ratan Tata and Ravi Kant had gone to Kolkata with an open mind, still believing that a solution favourable to all could be extracted from the mess that Singur had become. There was a final discussion, open and frank, with state government officials. It would be to no avail. Singur became a sacrificial victim and Tata Motors — after 18 months of unceasing endeavour, Rs15 billion of expenditure, and countless instances of undeserving distress — was left to carry the cross.

The Nano development team had begun planning for the worst even as the Singur situation started heating up. By December 2007, Girish Wagh could see some of the writing on the wall and he started working on a fallback arrangement should push come to punishment. Uttarakhand and Pune, both places where Tata Motors had full-fledged operations, were considered. It was decided that the engine would be manufactured at Pune and that the rest of the car, including final assembly, would happen in Uttaranchal. But, in the wake of the October 3 denouement, a far more critical question needed answering: where could the Nano find a new home, and quickly?

"We started scouting for an alternate location about a month before the pullout announcement, but not with any real seriousness," says Wagh. "Most of us were still hanging on to the hope that we would stay in Singur; after all, we had an almost-commissioned plant. We were not quite prepared to think otherwise." That would change in a hurry. "We were getting calls from different states right after Mr Tata's announcement, even before he left Kolkata," says Amarjit Singh Puri, the point person for liaisons. "Maharashtra, Gujarat, Andhra Pradesh and Karnataka, all of them welcomed us."

The next four days were a blur of hectic effort for managing director Ravi Kant and a small team of Tata Motors seniors, including Wagh and Puri. They were charged with finalising in double-quick time a decision that would ordinarily have taken many months to make. "We were flying about so much, with half-day meetings in one state and then rushing to another," says Puri. "It was challenging, it was exciting and we were honest with everybody about our expectations."

Dharwad in Karnataka, which had been considered as a possible site for the Nano plant before Singur happened, came into the picture once again, but the uneven terrain there led to it being ruled out. Other sites, too, were evaluated, but none of these could match what was on offer at Sanand in Gujarat, a two-hour drive from Ahmedabad and separated by a million miles in temperament and political culture from Singur. The biggest advantage with the site at Sanand was that it had about 1,100 acres in a flat stretch under a single land survey number. Progress was swift once the decision on the site had been made. By October 7, a mere 96 hours after that dark day in Kolkata, the deal was sealed.

"The speed with which things moved was phenomenal," says Puri. "Narendra Modi [the chief minister of Gujarat] runs the state much like a professional chief executive of a company. Once we had his backing, everyone in the state administration was aligned to the cause. He told us, 'This is not just your project; it is our project.' The whole process showed there are governments in India that mean business, that are supportive of business. We wanted to take the project to a place where it would be welcome. We didn't want this feeling that we were being given shelter, that we were refugees."

The political environment aside, the Sanand site had other positives to deliver to Tata Motors. The land is firmer, the soil is better for setting up an industrial facility, the property is not low lying, and the highway is 500 metres away, not so close, as in Singur, for disruptions to be caused easily. Add to that the ready availability of the land.

"Given what had unfolded in Singur, we paid careful attention, while choosing the new site, to the political climate in the state," says Wagh. "We also considered the mindset on industry, on entrepreneurship." The difference in Gujarat, as Tata Motors sees it, was the bipartisanship, the consensus on critical issues that benefit the entire state, as opposed to favouring a particular political grouping. "That is the nature of difference in the polity of the two states," says Kant. "In Gujarat, and so too in Maharashtra and elsewhere, when a big project sets up there is coming together of political opinion. That has never been the case in West Bengal."

Unity of purpose characterised, yet again, the fresh efforts the small-car team had to put in to make Sanand what Singur was supposed to be, the hub from where the Nano would roll out. Tata Motors took possession of the Sanand land on November 5, 2008, and, a day later, got started all over again on the gargantuan job of erecting and constructing a car-manufacturing facility. The spread was surveyed and a master plan, much of it borrowed wholesale from the drawings for Singur, was finalised. The manufacturing and planning lessons learned in Singur helped and, consequently, the speed with which work got done at the new facility was a lot faster.

"Singur was a tremendous learning experience," says Priyadarshan Kshirsagar, head of the manufacturing planning team on the Nano project. "It's difficult to admit, but we made some mistakes of an operational nature. Our endeavour at Sanand was to eliminate mistakes from day one, to improve execution and delivery over what they were at Singur." The second chance that the development team got meant that some small bit of rectitude could be salvaged from the larger waste that was Singur. "We listed out all the enhancements we could make to ensure we got things right the second time out," says Wagh. "We saw that most of what had gone wrong could be corrected. For example, at some places the height of the conveyers was not sufficient for the operators to work with. We made the necessary corrections at Sanand."

Dealing with, convincing and compensating the 50-odd vendors and suppliers who had followed Tata Motors to Singur was a different kind of issue. The losses they suffered at Singur may not have been as large as that which Tata Motors had to bear, but there is no doubting the shock the episode dealt. Worse, this happened at a time when the global economic slowdown was hurting automobile component manufacturers more than most and the large volumes the Nano promised were failing to materialise. Tata Motors worked out financial packages to compensate its vendors, but these can never in full measure make up for the troubles they had to cope with.

"We wanted to help our vendors come out of this stronger," says Wagh. "We wanted to repay their faith in us. We were looking beyond the launch of the car; we needed to improve it further, se-cure more cost reductions and develop new variants. A lot of work remains to be done and our vendors are going to remain critical to the programme." Tata Motors has also had significant contribu-tions coming from machinery and equipment suppliers, especially with all the dismantling and reinstalling that the Singur pullout brought about.

A third set of partners were the service providers, those run-ning canteens, transportation and the like. "The catering con-tractor started by supplying food for 10-20 people," says Wagh. "This went up to 600, to 1,300 and crossed 2,000, and then it dwin-dled to a point where there were just five of us left. You can imag-ine the kind of investment he would have had to make, and then see it come crashing down." What did not come crashing down was the infrastructure of the Singur plant. This had to be brought down with delicate care, piece by piece, in an operation without parallel in the world of manufacturing.

To dismantle the plant, pack the tens of thousands of components that went into its making, and transport them in more than 3,000 trailer-trucks to the other end of the country, some 2,100km away — that was the spirit-sapping, mind-numbing task Tata Motors was forced to undertake over a four-month period towards the end of 2008. The crazy bit was that not a single fully complete and roadworthy Nano rolled out of the Singur facility before it had to be picked apart.

The man at the helm of the dismantling, moving and reinstalling project was manufacturing head Ramesh Vishwakarma, a veteran engineer who had joined Tata Motors as a trainee in 1979, left the organisation after five years and worked in Indonesia before completing the circle by returning to the company in early 2008. "Frankly, it was a boring job," he says. "The challenge, then, was to do this as fast as possible while maintaining the quality of the machinery. We had new machines and they had to stay new till they reached Sanand." The planning that preceded the shifting happened in Pune over 20 days. "We consulted the manufacturers of the machines, worked out how to prevent rusting, laid out a dismantling process."

Vishwakarma uses words such as integrity and traceability to describe how his team went about the task. "Parts would be taken down and displayed, they would be tagged and photographed, then packed and loaded onto the trucks in a prescribed manner. The way we functioned, I could at any point of time find the part I was looking for. We tracked the trucks carrying the materials meticulously. We imposed control and order on what could have been a chaotic process. We had to be sure, when we opened the boxes, first of all that it contained what we expected it to contain and, two, that its quality had not been compromised."

A pad was carved out over 35 acres of land about 20km from

Sanand. This storage area, the first construction activity that happened for the new facility, was where the trucks would deposit their cargo. In March 2009, the shifting got started. The team scouted two routes and then settled for the Golden Quadrilateral way that crisscrosses through West Bengal, Jharkhand, Bihar, Uttar Pradesh and Rajastan before reaching Gujarat. This was the longer route, stretching more than 2,100km, but the quality of roads was better. "We were lucky in that we did not have any accidents," says Vishwakarma.

The first lot to be transported was the engine manufacturing machinery and infrastructure, which began in August 2008 itself, before the pullout decision was finalised. This lot was moved to Pune, so that production could begin there while Sanand was being put in order. By the new year the engines for the Nano were already being manufactured in Pune, and by August 2009 some 200 units were being rolled out. "The reason we chose Pune as a temporary arrangement was that it allowed us to better control and monitor this most critical of components in the car," says Sanjay Sablok, the power train specialist on the small-car project.

The utility infrastructure — transformers, compressors, power panels, electric cables, etc — preceded the arrival in Sanand of other material and equipment. Meanwhile, Jaydeep Desai and his colleagues from the manufacturing and planning group were working overtime to shut down the paint shop in Singur. This was complicated. "Keeping paint and chemicals without any processing is environmentally hazardous," explains Desai. "We had to keep the paint alive, which means keeping it in continuous circulation for three-four hours a day, till we could shift it to a safe place. Without this the paint would have gone bad. We did this for four months before taking the entire paint shop from Singur to Lucknow, where a requirement had come up."

The efforts of Desai and his team saved Tata Motors close to Rs5 million, but the tougher responsibility was disposing the waste chemicals generated in keeping the paint alive. "We neutralised the chemicals with the help of our suppliers and environmental bodies of the state government." The paint shop story symbolises, in a small way, the loss that Singur came to represent. A typical paint shop, one that can manage 1,200 car bodies in a day, takes 30 months to set up and can cost up to Rs3 billion. The Nano team had, in an exceptional endeavour, established the Singur paint operations in eight months and for under Rs500 million, albeit with a capacity of around 250 car bodies a day. "We actually painted just six bodies before we dismantled the shop," says Atul Vaidya, the planning engineer who would, on another day, let his emotions get the better of him.

By the end of May the dismantling and moving job had been completed and reinstallation could begin in Sanand. Tata Motors had not had to bring in consultants and other outsiders to help with the relocation. "This was a black box for us, we were not certain about what to do and how to do it, but we were able to cope," says Vishwakarma. "We had a strategy and a philosophy. We were aggressive in lowering transportation costs, we detailed everything that could go wrong, and we accounted for every nut and bolt. The only damage was had during the dismantling process in Singur was with a forklift. No other setbacks, none at all."

By August 2009, about 70 per cent of the reinstallation work had been completed. By November, pilot production was ready to begin. By February 2010, the first Nano was ready to be driven out of the Sanand facility. "What we have experienced with the shifting and reinstalling has been unique, but it's not an experience I would want to go through ever again," says Vishwakarma.

Neither would Tata Motors want a replication of what many in the organisation say has been the toughest part of the shift to Sanand: the troubles its people had to undergo when they were forced to uproot themselves and their families and start afresh with life in a new and unfamiliar place. Homes had to found and school admissions fixed, working spouses had to quit their jobs and hope for the best, long-term plans had to be forgotten as short-term exigencies took precedence.

There were people who had come to Singur for the project — from Chennai, from Pune, from Mumbai and many other places — and settled down in Kolkata. The October 3 decision meant moving in the middle of the academic year, and there was no option but to move. Production had to start from the facility in Uttarakhand, so people were required there. Additional hands were needed for the power train shop in Pune, and there was the new plant in Sanand to worry about. There were long deliberations before a plan was worked out. This did not, and could not, have satisfied all of those affected, especially those with grown-up children, but there was no option but to deal with the crisis.

Sablok, the power train engineer, had a particularly harrowing time with the shifting situation. Sablok had moved to Kolkata from Lucknow at the beginning of the 2008-09 academic year and his son, an only child, was readying for his standard 10 board exams when the Singur shutdown happened. "My family had been opposed to the move and we were having problems with teachers and the language," says Sablok. "In January I was asked to come to Pune and help out with the installation of the new engine facility. When my son's exams started I was shuttling between Pune and Kolkata so I could be with him and help him at least during the most crucial papers. I was flying in and out." In July 2009, Sablok, his wife and son shifted to Ahmedabad. Ten days after the move, he had to leave his family and go back to Pune.

What Sablok had to go through was the rule as the engineers and others working on the Nano project struggled to adjust to the circumstances. The troubles in Singur had families on edge and while many welcomed the decision to go, this caused its own share of anxiety. "After the launch of the car I did mention in interviews the contribution our colleagues had made, their struggles in the face of the Singur adversity, but no one found this spicy enough to publish," says Wagh. "For us workers the shifting was easier than it was for the families. We were going to a similar kind of work environment, meeting the same people, but their lives changed completely. Yet somehow the team held together. I think we lost only 1-2 per cent of our people during this time."

Once the dust of the relocation effort began to settle, the small-car team came to appreciate what Sanand had to offer. "West Bengal had a lot going for it, but Gujarat has proved far better for us," says Jaydeep Desai. "People work harder here and the general attitude is so different." There were other advantages. "I've come to believe that whatever has happened has happened for the good," says Girish Wagh. "First of all there is the relief that we were back on track. Second, we got time to refine the product. Third, we were able to test our hypotheses about our processes and to deal with quality issues. Also, we have come to appreciate and understand what it means to operate out of multiple locations. We have had to change the way we work. It has been a big learning."

The $417 million Sanand facility is what is termed an intelligent automation plant. This 'smart factory' relies on intelligent-automation hardware, software and services provided by the American company, Rockwell Automation Inc. The technology has more to it than robotics and the plant manages all sensors, microchips and motor controls, predicting bottlenecks and breakdowns on the factory floor before they take place. It has the capacity to order parts from suppliers to keep up with production orders and a 'genealogy' feature that tracks every part in every car, allowing Tata Motors to trace vehicles that may have a defective component.

The automation technology at the heart of the Sanand facility will, in time to come, enable it to plug into smart electrical grids and synchronise production with the cheapest and most plentiful supplies of energy. "Such a feature might seem obvious, but it's new and novel to many," said Vinay Rangarajan, a Rockwell engineer, in an interview with the *Milwaukee Journal Sentinel*.[1] This is cutting-edge stuff, but it wasn't easy for Rockwell to bag the Tata Motors contract (it had to overcome competition from Siemens and General Electric, two of the world's best-known technology enterprises). Rangarajan expects Tata Motors to build more smart factories, in South Africa, Thailand and Indonesia, to manufacture the Nano.

Wagh, however, is quick to point out that all the silver linings in the world cannot make up for the loss and the frustration Singur inflicted on the Nano project. "The situation there dragged our attention away from what should have been our focus and that affected our engineering preparedness on the product. It was so distracting. Personally speaking, though, I've been able to put Singur behind me, mostly because I haven't had the time or any space in the mind to think about it."

Wagh and his colleagues have warm words for the manner in which Ratan Tata stood by them as the crisis deepened. "He stuck to his conviction," says the leader of the Nano development programme. "He did not allow us to get pushed around. He could have said our team should have handled the situation better, and there were things we could have done better, but he never did that.

Ratan Tata and Ravi Kant could not come to Kolkata during those end days, so they were dependent on the information we were giving them. They backed us to the hilt."

As for the site at Singur, it now resembles an industrial wasteland. Puri is certain that, in time, the people who fuelled and drove the agitation will come to realise their folly. "We were always willing to talk." Debasis Ray, the corporate communication head, concurs with his colleague. "Maybe things could have been done differently, but I don't think the agitation ought to have been taken to a stage where we had to leave. There could have been a resolution. It was short-sighted politics. This had little to do with the development of West Bengal."

Ray, himself a Bengali, contends that the state he hails from is virulently partisan in its politics. "I don't think there has been any occasion when politics there has been bipartisan. I would submit that there are several states where different parties and different political contest vigorously, but they come together when the development of the state is at stake. That isn't the case in West Bengal. As for us, we walked out with our chin up, with no erosion in the goodwill the Tatas have enjoyed for the last hundred years and more."

"We went to West Bengal in good faith and with the best of intentions; we wanted to demonstrate our sincerity and commitment to the state," says former Tata Motors managing director Ravi Kant. "If at all we can be faulted, it is in that we did not understand the politics there. We did not foresee the political situation that would unfold, but then, who could have?"

January 2008: Ratan Tata at the unveiling of the Nano

2003-04: Early renderings of the small car

June 2004: One of the earliest ideas of what the small car could be

January 2006: Nano's design begins to take shape

January 2008: The Nano's unveiling at the Delhi Auto Expo witnessed an explosion of media interest

The Nano: A marvel of innovation

March 2009: The launch of the Nano at the Parsi Gymkhana in Mumbai

March 2009: The Nano team with Ratan Tata at the launch in Mumbai

April 2009: The first Nano rolls out from the Pantnagar plant in Uttaranchal

July 2009: Ashok Vichare, owner of the first Nano

June 2010: The Nano rolls out from the plant at Sanand in Ahmedabad, Gujarat

CHAPTER 5
The first look

Presenting a newborn to the world may not have meant so much to so many as it did when Ratan Tata drove his dream to centre stage at the Delhi Auto Expo on a winter morning in 2008. The nip in the air wasn't all down to the weather. The crowd packing the pavilion at Pragati Maidan for the January 10 unveiling of what had been dubbed in advance as the "people's car" seemed to sense something exceptional was on its way. And the rock-star greeting the Tata Motors chairman received — the cheers and the whistles drowning the polite applause from the coiffured front row — as he steered a pearly white Nano into the limelight announced the arrival of a truly unique motor car.

The Delhi Auto Expo is usually a bustling affair, attended by ordinary folk as well as aficionados and those associated with the automobile industry. But the 2008 edition was biggest ever, and the reason was the Nano. The crowd at the unveiling comprised people from across the societal spectrum: government ministers, business bosses and foreign dignitaries, motoring enthusiasts and media professionals, celebrities and ordinary folk, even tourists taking a detour to get their eyes on the 'Tata car'. They came from all parts of India and a fair share from abroad, drawn by curiosity and conjecture about what Rs1 lakh could deliver by way of an automobile on four wheels.

For all their planning ahead of the event, the people at Tata Motors were overwhelmed by the response. They had never anticipated the rush, the outpouring of interest and accolades, the multitude of visitors wanting to see, touch and feel the Nano. As for the team that had created the small car, the experience of the unveiling brought with it satisfaction and relief in equal measure. Girish Wagh, the head of the Nano development programme, and his team had been filled with hope and expectation, emotion and not a little trepidation as they faced their moment of engineering truth. Now they could rest a moment and soak up the acclaim.

"In the days leading up to the unveiling, and especially the night before it, somewhere in our minds there was this concern about how people would react to the car," says Wagh. "We were thinking, 'What's going to happen?' We were nervous, we were worked up, and then this response ... We were swept away. We had an inkling that people would be surprised by the car, the look of it. We had shown the Nano to some outsiders prior to the unveiling and they had been suitably impressed. So we knew there would be a wow effect, but nothing like what happened, particularly so with the publicity the car got internationally. It was mind-boggling."

Many hundreds of thousands of visitors thronged the expo over the ten days of the event, and everyone wanted to get a glimpse of the Nano. The organisers asked Tata Motors to organise an additional exhibit of the car at a different venue just so the pressure of the crowds could ease. The Tata team doubled the number of staff at its pavilion to cope with the weekend rush. "Every query would begin and end with the Nano," recalls Gurpal Singh, a senior executive with the Confederation of Indian Industry, one of the organisers of the Expo. "The crowd attendance was a record for the event. At the weekend we had 180,000 people by 12 noon." The Nano pavilion had to be closed for about two hours to control the surge.

Keetsa Mattress, an American tourist who managed to jostle her way through the throng to the Nano turntable, was quoted as saying: "I don't necessarily care about the car, but I wanted to celebrate the awesomeness that is the word 'lakh'. Jimmy Yep, a South Korean, took one look at the Nano and declared it would change the way the world views developing countries. Indian visitors were more personal about what the car meant to them. "If I can get a loan from my boss, I might buy the car so I don't have to take my mother on my motorcycle anymore," said Daniel Abraham.

Debasis Ray, Tata Motors' corporate communications head, recalls a visitor getting the shock of his life when he discovered Ratan Tata giving him advice on the Nano that would best suit him. "We had these touchscreen kiosks where people could check out different options for the car, colours, accessories and the like," says Ray. "This gentleman was trying to decide which colour Nano he liked and a voice from behind urged him to go for red. He turned around and saw it was Mr Tata doing the prompting. He almost fell at the chairman's feet. 'You are god,' he started saying. 'Here, take my cheque and give me a car.' We were not ready for that kind of reaction."

RG Rajhans, part of the body systems engineering group with the small-car programme — and one of the nine Tata Motors engineers who followed Ratan Tata to the stage at the unveiling in two different Nanos — believes there was a patriotic element to the crowd going gaga over the vehicle. "It was seen as India's car rather than a Tata product," he says. "Within 30 minutes of the unveiling I was receiving calls from relatives and friends, some of them settled abroad, asking about the car and my involvement with it. I was surprised, to say the least. The world was watching, the news spread so fast."

Seven show cars were manufactured for the Delhi unveiling, five for the show itself and two as backup. These special Nanos did not roll off an assembly line; they were crafted with discipline and care in a prototype shop at Tata Motors' Engineering Research Centre in Pune. This was an operation shrouded in secrecy. "We did not want to dilute the fun of the car being seen for the very first time at the Expo," says Nikhil Jadhav, a member of the Nano design team. "There was a lot of security and cellphones were not allowed." About 100 people were permitted access to the shop, yet not a single photograph of the car, or even the nametag that would define it, was revealed."

The naming of the Nano was no small task. The process began in early 2007, a year before the unveiling, when Jadhav and others in the styling studio came up with a list of 35-40 names and sent it to Bombay House, the Tata headquarters in Mumbai. The naming of a vehicle is usually the privilege of the marketing department, but the Nano's design guys wanted to keep things close to their chest.

"We had reference points while choosing the names and the Rs1-lakh price was a factor," says Jadhav. "Some of the names we had on the list were vague, some were strange, some were interesting, some were recycled, some were acronyms. There was Mint,

Nio, Inca, Mycar, ICar, Eon, Era, Atom and there was Nano. We wanted it to be small and nice, easy off the tongue."

The long list of names was shortened to four and checked and cross-checked to ensure there were no copyright problems. Ratan Tata had stationed himself in Pune 15 days before the Expo, checking every detail of the show cars and going over the presentation he had to make. This was when the name was decided. The styling pros had been working on the font for the nametag when, one evening, Ratan Tata walked into the design studio. "We settled for the Bauhaus font, with all the letters in lower case, just as he wanted it," says Jadhav. "He would spend three-four hours every evening at the plant, getting updates, discussing this and that. That's when we got the design for the mascots frozen and the Nano name was finalised."

The lettering of the nametags had to be done in chrome and a Pune agency was contracted for the job. Jadhav was apprehensive that the name would be leaked to the media, so he rearranged the alphabets when he sent the nametag. It wasn't much of a deterrent, but it did the trick. "We fixed the nametags and the mascots at 2am on the night before the car went on display," says Jadhav.

The show cars were transported from Pune to Delhi in three trailers from January 4 with security guards riding shotgun. This was another top-secret operation, something that Tata Motors and the small-car team were getting more and more adept at. In Delhi the cars were parked in a warehouse, where they stayed till the night before the unveiling. "It was all hush-hush," says Jadhav. "The cars were, of course drivable, but they were never driven. There were photographers snooping around so we brought them to the expo pavilion in the trailers and then we worked on accessories and the final detailing." Despite all the precautions, the car's name did leak out (a television channel got its hands on that juicy nugget). "But the car's shape and styling, how it looked — no one other than us knew about that."

Ratan Tata was in the thick of things while all the readying of the show cars was happening. "He was involved in every aspect of the unveiling," says Girish Wagh. "In Delhi, the night before the unveiling, he was there with us right up to 2am. We had been rehearsing how the cars would come on stage, who would be where, etc, and he stayed with us right through. We came back at 9am on the morning of the unveiling and he was there before us, working on his presentation and rehearing his part." And then the chairman changed the programme.

"I was in the audience and Mr. Tata was in this waiting area behind the dais," recalls Wagh. "It was around 10am and the show was close to beginning when I got a message that he wanted to see me. I went up there and he was with (then Tata Motors managing director) Ravi Kant. He said he wouldn't be driving out to the stage in a red standard-version Nano, as had been decided; that he would come in a pearly white top-end model. I don't know why he did that." The chairman had his reasons, as he did for the list of bulleted points he had jotted down on a piece of paper for the post-presentation speech he had to make, unusual for somebody who spoke extempore on such occasions. But this was no ordinary occasion.

The unveiling began with a pre-recorded, 11-minute message from Ratan Tata that was projected on a giant screen. The chairman — a person who has become proficient with such presentations over time, rather than possessing any innate talent for it — touched on a variety of subjects: innovation, the first manned flight, the progress from bicycles to motorised two wheelers, the invention of computers, the family-of-the-scooter story, his quest for an affordable and safe mode of transport and the conceptual evolution of the Nano. He also spoke about the doubters and naysayers — a clip of the putdown by Osamu Suzuki, the chairman of Suzuki, ran during this portion — and the pollution his small car would allegedly unleash.

The talking done, Ratan Tata, in person this time, drove his Nano to the stage as the spotlights shone and the theme from Stanley Kubrick's *2001: A Space Odyssey* played in the background. Nine Tata Motors engineers, in a red and a yellow Nanos followed, flanking the chairman as he eased his big frame out of his vehicle. "It would be but fair and fitting to recognise and acknowledge the achievement of the young group of engineers who undertook the challenge for four years with great sacrifice to themselves and produced this car," he said before inviting Girish Wagh to the stage.

The cheers from the crowd reached a crescendo and Ratan Tata had to nearly shout to be heard as he explained the logic of the Nano name and, to the loudest clapping at the show, made his "promise is a promise" commitment on the Rs1-lakh price tag for the small car. The unveiling had been a simple affair, without any banging of the drum or tall claims. "There are no celebrities for this function, nor any dance number," said Ratan Tata. "The centre of attraction is our new car... We are happy to present the people's car to India and we hope it brings the joy, pride and utility of owning a car to families who need personal mobility."

Ratan Tata did not leave it at that. The combative mood the chairman was in — brought on, without doubt, by the flak he had to face prior to the unveiling on everything from safety and emissions to climate change and gridlock — showed in the comments he made after the event. "Take [the Nano] as it is," he was quoted as saying by one publication. "If we do have competition, and it looks like we will, I think it will be a vindication of what we set out to do. I hope that any battle is in the marketplace in an open manner. I am quite willing to fight in the marketplace. I also urge all players to fight there. If that happens, and if we succeed, we will have broken new ground for India."

The way Girish Wagh remembers it, the unveiling was as much Ratan Tata's baby as the star of the show, the Nano. "He had it choreographed down to the last detail," says the small car's project leader. "He was presenting his car, his dream to the entire world and he wanted everything to be perfect. He rehearsed the routine thrice and he reworked the script the agency had come up with. He had seen the first cut of the audiovisual two days before the unveiling and he was very unsatisfied." That's when Ratan Tata specifically asked for the *Space Odyssey* theme. He had the length of the presentation cut and demanded that its focus be on people. "He did not want it to be flashy."

Wagh was close at hand to see that Ratan Tata was not quite his usual self on the morning of the unveiling. "There was plenty of negative publicity ahead of the Expo and he was obviously hurt," he says, "and so too were many of us. We were trying to accomplish a tremendously difficult task and here were these people trying to bring us down. The chairman's words were emotionally charged and I think the audience grasped that."

RG Rajhans, the body systems engineer who was in the yellow Nano that followed the chairman's car onto the stage, took a little less serious approach to the whole affair. "We were supposed to park the car on the stage, open the door and come out and stand beside it," he says. "We were joking that the door would not open, that we would be trapped inside and the mob outside would break through and jump all over the car." Wagh, a reserved person who is less than comfortable on a public stage, did not have any such luxury of lightening up. Ratan Tata had told him before the unveiling began that he would be calling him to the stage later in the show. It wasn't an idea he welcomed.

"I had kind of requested him not to have me on the stage, but his mind was made up," says Wagh. "Earlier, I was supposed to come in one of the two other cars with other team members. Then he said, 'No, you stay in the audience. I'm going to call you separately.' He had been saying all along that whatever else the Nano may have represented, it was also a tribute to the young engineers who worked on the project. He said that calling me and the others to the stage was one way of showcasing what had been achieved. Getting up there that day — I was overwhelmed. It certainly has been the greatest recognition I have ever received."

A heavier burden for Wagh was deciding who else from his 500-strong, extended team would share the stage with him. The decision was that there would be 10 team members on the stage, including Wagh, and it was up to the project leader to choose who they would be. "I was in a fix. I could not go by hierarchy; and there were so many to pick from. I discussed it with the chairman and others and this went on for three days. Finally, Ravi Kant got fed up and asked me to stop hemming and hawing and make up my mind. He told me, 'You have to take decisions continuously in life and you can't take such a simple one?' So I did my best balancing act and made my choice."

Wagh felt he needed to keep all sections of the team happy. "I tried to ensure that every group on the project was represented, and it never was about having department bosses come up." The group that Wagh settled on finally comprised GR Nagabhushan, head of passenger car engineering, Abhay M Deshpande, the vehicle integration chief, Jay Bolar, the point person for integration, Rajhans from body engineering, MB Kulkarni from construction, E Balasubramaniam of the sourcing team, Priyadarshan Kshirsagar, head of the manufacturing group, Jaydeep Desai from planning and NK Jain from engine development. "I did not get any complaints so I guess it was a good selection," says Wagh.

This kind of recognition has now become the norm at every launch from the Tata Motors stable, Wagh adds. "Calling people up on stage began with the Nano. Till then we had only the top management and the chairman. It makes a difference to have team members get up to the stage and take a bow. It's well-deserved recognition. They deserve to be there."

For the wider Tata Motors organisation, there was more than recognition that followed in the wake of the Nano's unveiling. "We had journalists squatting on the floor in a hall that could seat 200 people," says corporate communication head Debasis Ray of the rush at press conferences during the course of the expo. "We had government functionaries, foreign dignitaries and lay people thronging the pavilion. Often I would see this surprise on their faces when they first encountered the Nano. It was extraordinary."

Ray recalls an instance when the Tata Motors enclosure had shut for the day and there was this family with two children who wanted to see the car. "The father told us they had come all the way from Agra for a sight of the Nano, so we let them in through the back entrance. We removed the veil from the vehicle and the kids started running around the car. We had many such experiences."

Ray, a veteran of numerous media engagements, says he had never seen anything like the crowd at the press conference that was organised on January 10 after the unveiling, but that was only till a little more than a year later, when the Nano was officially launched at the Taj Mahal Palace and Tower in Mumbai on March 23, 2009. "There were some 800 journalists from across the world, from Russia, from Japan, from Iceland even. I was stunned."

The unveiling at the Expo sparked an explosion of interest in the Nano that may have abated, but the people who caught the stardust from that remarkable event still remember it for all kinds of reasons. C Ramakrishnan, a financial whiz who got drafted in to coordinate the small-car development programme during its embryonic days, had tears welling up in his eyes as the Nano rolled into view. "I have been with the company for 30 years," says the chief financial officer of Tata Motors, "and I had never got so emotional. I have no doubt that many others in the company felt that way."

For Girish Wagh, the applause and the adulation were swiftly followed by recognition of the accountability Tata Motors had on its hands in the aftermath of the unveiling. "The response that we got, from the media, from people in India and abroad, made us realise the responsibility we carried of delivering on the promise of the Nano," he says. This did not mean that everyone was sold on the small car there and then — *Wired* magazine quoted Wagh as saying, "Can you believe it? At the expo, people actually began tapping on [the Nano] to see if it was made of metal." — but the reception it received and the consequent attention showered on it made it a lot more than just another motor car.

There was a time when only the wealthy could own an automobile. The Ford Model T changed that equation for good. A hundred years down the line, the Nano holds the potential to touch the lives of a multitude of people in a country where distances are vast, public transport is patchy and roads terribly unsafe. There are many bridges to be crossed, though, before Tata Motors can rest easy. As the company's chairman said in the days after the frenzy at the unveiling had begun to dissipate, "The final judgment will be made by the consumer. Let's wait and let them decide."

CHAPTER **6**

The world reacts

osannas to the automobile gods would have been in order for everyone involved in the Nano development programme as a watching world showered attention and acclaim on their labour of engineering love in the wake of its unveiling at the Delhi Auto Expo. There was criticism, too, but the wet blankets failed to douse the exhilaration engendered by a product with the potential, evident even at that stage, to change the rules of the motoring game.

The small-car team felt vindicated. To say the reaction surprised the people at Tata Motors would be an understatement; they were overwhelmed, floored by the flood of interest in a vehicle that struck a chord with everyday car enthusiasts as much as auto mavens and industry gurus. There would be no damning by faint praise, anything lukewarm or halfhearted in the manner of the response to the Nano. Here was a car that had stretched the definition of extreme engineering like never before, and the exuberance that greeted its showcasing was well-deserved, if not entirely expected.

The scrum around the Nanos on display at the expo reflected the general public's enthusiasm for a car they could justifiably claim as India's own, a homegrown winner crafted on a workbench of challenges that would have defeated a lesser endeavour. "For millions of people in the developing world, Tata Motors' new $2,500 four-door subcompact — the world's cheapest car — may yield a transportation revolution as big as Henry Ford's Model T," wrote Gavin Rabinowitz of the *Associated Press*. "It is a potentially gigantic development if it delivers what has been promised," said John Casesa of the Casesa Shapiro Group, a New York-based auto industry advisory firm. "I think there is immense unmet demand for a vehicle of this type, because it effectively eliminates the great leap currently required to go from a two-wheel to a four-wheel vehicle. [Tata Motors is] creating something that has never existed before, the utility of a car with the affordability of a motorcycle."

"The Nano is a great symbol of Indian-*ishtyle* socialism," gushed *rediff.com*. *Time* magazine was more elaborate. "It could well be one of the most important cars ever designed... Even before it goes on sale, [the car] has become an important symbol of an emerging trend in the developing world, a new brand of innovation that makes more out of less and engineers clever but cheap fixes to problems that Western companies might throw expensive technology at." It went on to quote Ratan Tata, the Tata Motors chairman who had staked his reputation and much more on the car, on why he thought the Nano was more evolution rather revolution. "If you asked me if it would be possible to build a lower-cost car than this — a car, say, for Rs50,000 — I might be driven to say, 'Yes, it might be possible.' I don't think anything's impossible."

Newsweek, Time's renowned rival, called the Nano a "new breed of 21st-century cars" that embody "a contrarian philosophy of smaller, lighter, cheaper that portend a new era in inexpensive personal transportation". *The Financial Times* linked the car to the emergence into global prominence of the country where it was created. "If ever there were a symbol of India's ambitions to become a modern nation, it would surely be the Nano, the tiny car with the even tinier price tag," it said. "The Nano encapsulates the dream of millions of Indians groping for a shot at urban prosperity."

India's political class, never one to miss out on the opportunity to attach itself to success stories, was effusive in extolling the Nano. "This is a proud moment for India," said commerce minister Kamal Nath. "It demonstrates India's technological and entrepreneurial ability. It fulfils the need of the common Indian who aspires to move from a two-wheeler to a four-wheeler." Writing in an editorial in his party mouthpiece, *Saamna*, Bal Thackeray, the Shiv Sena supremo, doffed his hat to Ratan Tata. "There are many rich and super-rich industrialists in the country… but not all can touch the hearts of the common people like [Mr Tata]," he said.

Business bosses and automobile industry executives, in particular, were, by and large, receptive to the idea of the Nano. "The car has put India on the global map," said Fionna Prims, head of business development for Segment Y, an automotive consultant for emerging markets. "[Tata Motors] has done in four years what the Japanese took 30 years to do. It will change the whole industry." Ashvin Chotai, a London-based auto analyst, was more circumspect. "The proof of the pudding will be in driving it, but visually it looks pretty good," he said. "The pricing was a bit of a surprise. I thought it would be a bit higher." Shravan Garg, group editor of Bhaskar Publications, saw the Nano as more than a car. "It's a vehicle of change," he said. "It will change the face of society in India."

Gal Luft, an alternative energy campaigner in Washington — and a less-than-popular personality in gas-guzzling Detroit — made his appreciation amply clear. "A century after Henry Ford put America on wheels with the Model T, the affordable Tata Nano is doing the same for the less privileged of the world," he said "What is now dismissed by many as a 'toy car' could soon reveal itself to be the mouse that roared, one of the most transformational consumer products of the century… The low sticker price [of the car] means a 65 per cent increase in the number of Indian families who can now afford a car. But India is not the only hub of poverty, and what works for its middle class could appeal to those in Bangladesh, Pakistan, Sri Lanka, Guatemala, Congo and scores of other countries, including China…"

"It's a red-letter day for Indian industry, a day India should be proud of," said Venu Srinivasan, chairman of motorcycle manufacturer TVS Motors. "Ratan Tata has the vision to create a new business model and all the naysayers are looking at it with concern. The Nano is a path breaker." SM Bafna, managing director of Bafna Motors, an auto dealer in Mumbai, revealed that he had to keep his phone off the hook to get some respite from prospective buyers. "People are desperately waiting for the car," he said.

The reactions to the Nano from Tata Motors' competitors ranged from the magnanimous to the petty to the downright nasty. An official of Hyundai Motors said he saw the car as "definitely impacting our sales". Rajiv Bajaj, the managing director of Bajaj Auto sweated on Tata Motors' behalf over the commercial viability of the Nano. "My scepticism about the Tata car is not about Tata's ability to put it together, but to put it together at the price of Rs1 lakh," he said. "I still haven't heard [Tata Motors] say it will be profitable."

The most churlish of the Tata-bashing cabal was Osamu Suzuki, the chairman of Suzuki Motor Corporation, whose Maruti-800 suffered plenty in comparison with the Nano. Suzuki had dismissed the concept of the Tata small car while it was being developed, initially proclaiming that it would not be possible and, later, saying it could never be made safe enough, or good enough to survive the competition. Jagidsh Khattar, the former chief of Maruti Suzuki, the Indian arm of Suzuki, was less vituperative. "[The Nano] is a good product, but it's still too early to say whether it will overtake the [Maruti-800] because it caters to a totally new market segment," he said after the Delhi unveiling.

Debasis Ray, Tata Motors' corporate communications head, says the company took a deliberate decision not to respond to Suzuki's barbs. "He was speaking without any knowledge of the product," he says. "We did not react till the very last time. We did not want to speak about the car until it was displayed. We were sure it would speak for itself."

The passage of time would not diminish the distaste Maruti Suzuki appeared to have for the Nano. Speaking in an interview[1] with *Mint* newspaper in April 10, 2010, more than two years after the small car was presented at the Delhi Auto Expo, company chairman RC Bhargava tried to catch smoke in a butterfly net. "The Nano has been around for nine months, but I don't hear the buzz associated with a hit product," he said. "Any car which is in hot demand has a premium. The Nano does not. So that somehow makes me believe that this car requires more work before it becomes the phenomenon it was touted to be." Should not the sub-lakh car have come from Maruti, he was asked, to which he replied. "No, because we came to the conclusion that we couldn't do it."

An exception to such spite was Carlos Ghosn, head of the Nissan-Renault combine, who was generous in his commendation of the Nano and candid in saying there was a lot his company could learn from Tata Motors and its trailblazing product. "[The Nano is] a very good first concept of what should be a popular car for emerging markets," said the man credited with coining the term 'frugal engineering' in an interview[2] to *Business Line* newspaper, adding that the development of the car "is something that is very promising not only for India but for other emerging markets also". Ghosn went on to say that his engineers had cut the Nano into "I don't know how many pieces" to learn how Tata Motors had managed to pull off the seemingly impossible.

A different fusillade of criticism the Nano has had to live with is its supposed potential, by way of the numbers it would sell, to pollute and to burden India's rickety urban infrastructure to breaking point. "I am having nightmares [about the car]," said Rajendra Pachauri, head of the United Nations' Nobel Prize-winning Intergovernmental Panel on Climate Change, imprecating a vehicle that emits about 25 per cent less carbon dioxide per mile on average than a standard automobile on India's roads. "In my view this represents a bankruptcy of policy as far as transport options are concerned." Ratan Tata responded that Pachauri "need not have nightmares", pointing out that the Nano went beyond meeting emission standards in force in India.

The disapproval of the Nano on environmental grounds sprang mainly from an elite constituency of people who seemed aghast at the prospect of having to share the road with the hoi polloi. Ratan Tata and Tata Motors found support from many quarters in this

scrap. "The rich are responsible for vehicular pollution, conges-
tion and fuel emissions," said Bal Thackeray in a scathing attack
on the Nano's critics. "Why should the middle class be punished
… and prevented from realising their dream of owning a car?"

The Nano's appeal is to middle-class people everywhere, not
just India. "The global market for the Nano and similarly low-
priced cars could be immense — the World Bank counts more
than 800 million people who earn between $3,600 and $11,0000
annually," wrote Scott Carney in *Wired*[3]. "Sure, a single Nano is a
step toward independence, security and social mobility, but to
some observers, millions of Nanos spell apocalypse." Carney goes
on to quote Gaurav Gupta, commissioner of urban land transport
in Bangalore. "When the printing press came to Europe and everyone could suddenly buy a Bible, people in the church thought it
would be the end of religion. They were wrong," said Gupta in his
defence of the small car. "This is just like the Nano. It will make
cars affordable to many more people, and critics are scared. But we
will adjust. That is the way it has always been."

The *Wired* article also touched on the kind of competition the
Nano could expect in years to come. "Now that Tata Motors has
shown the way, competitors are scrambling to offer their own
budget vehicles. Hyundai has announced a $3,700 car. Renault-
Nissan has teamed with Indian motorcycle maker Bajaj to put
400,000 of its own ultra-low-cost cars on the road by 2011. General
Motors is rumoured to be working on a Nano-killer with China's
Wuling Automotive. A decade hence, millions of ultra-low-cost vehicles will crowd narrow alleyways throughout the world…" Carney put Ravi Kant, the former managing director of Tata Motors,
on the spot with his prognosis. What about traffic in such a sorry
scenario, he asked. "You know we also make buses, don't you?"
Kant replied. "We're happy to sell those, too."

In keeping with the zeitgeist, the Nano attracted
loads of attention in cyberspace, too, as bloggers and surfers
waded into arguments about the effect car the would have, the
changes it would herald and the prejudice it had to face. "I think
the Nano's 50mpg is an excellent example of a frugal car, one
which goes about its business with minimum wastage," wrote Au-
toindustrie, an anonymous blogger at autoindustrie.blogspot.com.
"Are [the car's] critics implying that Indians and Chinese cannot
own cars so that Americans can continue driving their gargantuan
trucks and sports utility vehicles while holding the title of the
largest CO_2 emitter in the world?

"History has shown that the automotive industry, mainly run
by old men in grey suits, is more likely to gang up and resist
change rather than to embrace it. Just as the 'big three' were hos-
tile to the first wave of Asian cars, the Japanese brands 40 years
ago, they will continue to resist India's entry into their big boys'
club... Now is an excellent time for Tata to challenge the established power plays. Once the industry has gone Nano, there is no
turning back."

Atul K Vaidya, a senior engineer with the planning team on the
Nano development programme, took a more personal view of what
the Nano might mean for ordinary people.

"A Mercedes Benz with a Rs60-lakh [Rs6 million] price tag is
something few people can afford, so there's this glamour attached
to it," he contends. "But there's glamour with the Nano, too, and
price is again the determining factor. The common man who gets
a Nano, through a lottery no less, has this feeling that he is part of
a revolution." Vaidya recalls two foreign delegations, one from Germany, the other from Thailand, going over the top after a drive in
the small car. "The Germans — they were paint-shop manufacturers — wrote to us after returning to their country, asking

whether they could have a Nano to display in their factory, along-side Porches, Alfa Romeos and the like."

Back on its home turf, the Nano had heads turning whenever it ventured out on the roads. Vikram Sinha, head of customer support at Tata Motors, remembers the overdose of attention the car got when he and his team went on a 5,000-km test drive over seven days in early 2008, a while after the unveiling at the expo. "There were five of us, all customer-care engineers, in three Nanos and we had others joining us for parts of the journey," says Sinha. The trip was exhilarating for Sinha and his men, with whoops of delight greeting their arrival in a town and people crowding around the cars wherever they stopped. "We would have kids shouting *'Nano ayee, Nano ayee* [the Nano has come]' and everybody would rush to the cars. It was a fantastic experience."

The customer-care team wanted to get a first-hand feel of how the Nano would behave when it was pushed to the limit on Indian roads. The three-car fleet took in mountain passes and plains, good weather and bad, remote interior roads and highways. "We covered 500-1,000 km in a day, starting from Pune and traversing Ahmedabad, Jaipur, Delhi, Chandigarh, Amritsar, Ambala, Naini-tal and Ranikhet before heading back to Delhi," says Sinha. "None of the cars gave any problem, but we did learn enough about them to make improvements."

The team had kept the test drive under wraps and tried to avoid publicity. That's not how it panned out, though. "We had the local media on us in most places we went," says Sinha. "We took the cars to the Golden Temple in Amritsar and we were surrounded. We also used the trip to meet some of our dealers and show them the cars." Arun Vartak of Pandit Auto, a Pune outlet that has been selling Tata Motors products since the 1960s, was just the kind of dealer Sinha and his team interacted with. "We decided to obtain a dealership for the Nano as soon as we saw the car at the Delhi Auto Expo," he says. "We had no doubt it would do great business."

Pandit Auto has sold some 30 Nanos and the number would have been a lot more without the production constraints that have shackled Tata Motors. "The response to the car has been extremely good," says Vartak. "People are eager to have their delivery as soon as possible. They want to show it to their neighbours and friends. Those that have got the car are happy, though we have had suggestions come in and small irritants to deal with. Some people were apprehensive in the initial phase; they thought they might have problems on steep gradients, but we have not had any complaints on that score. What we need right now is more cars to sell. We need to see many more Nanos on the road."

Amit Rathod, the owner of Rathod Motors in Vapi, Gujarat, echoes his Pune counterpart's views on the Nano and the impression it has left on people. Rathod, who has been a Tata Motors dealer for four years, was convinced the Nano made solid economic sense, to him as much as to ordinary buyers, after test-driving a demo vehicle. "In one word, it's revolutionary," he says. "It's value for money, an amazing product for the price at which it is being offered."

Rathod's dealership is on one of the arterial roads of Vapi and the day his first Nano was unloaded from the trailer there was an all-mighty traffic jam that choked the road outside his shop. It wasn't quite the kind of gridlock Rajendra Pachauri and those of his persuasion were raging against, but there it was. "I have never seen this sort of craze for a car, this sort of hysteria in my time in the business," says Rathod. "We have had people purchasing a Mercedes or a BMW and also wanting a Nano. Owning the car has become a matter of prestige."

This is the kind of news that has warmed the heart of Girish

Wagh, the leader of the Nano development programme. "It appears that people are generally happy with the car," he says. "Its roominess, its pickup, its air conditioning — our buyers have found these more than satisfactory. That's good, but there are some points for improvement, as we have been told by auto enthusiasts and journalists. We knew these points would come up and we have worked on them, especially the overall level of refinement."

For a few head-spinning weeks in the summer of 2009, Ashok Vichare, an official with the Indian government's customs and central excise department in Mumbai, lived the celebrity life given to India's cricket icons and Bollywood stars. Vichare became the proud possessor of the very first Nano, a silver-coloured model allotted through a lottery that pulled in 200,000 people. To say this lucky turn transformed his life may be an exaggeration, but it certainly delivered to Vichare his 15 minutes of fame, and then some.

"I bought my Nano without any test drive; I had complete faith in Ratan Tata's car," says Vichare, who took a loan from the State Bank of India to finance his Rs1.85-lakh, high-end version of the vehicle. "I'm possessive about my Nano; the only person to drive it other than me has been my daughter — on a single occasion. I don't even let someone else wash it; I do it myself." This is Vichare's first car and, the way he sees it, he could not have asked for more. "It's affordable, it's beautiful."

The middle-aged Vichare says he has enjoyed every single ride he has had in his Nano, and the ride he has been on ever since being picked in the lottery. "I've had media people swarming over me, many of them from abroad, from the United States, from France, from Germany. In the initial days, crowds would gather around the car at traffic signals. Once a stern policeman told me to move on and stop creating a jam. I was the centre of attraction, with my relatives, with neighbours, with everyone. The day I brought the car home, the road leading to the colony where I live was jammed with people."

For Harish Dayaram Thakur, a retired Reserve Bank of India official, the Nano was the first car he bought after selling his Maruti 800 nine years earlier. "I was comfortable travelling in taxis and autorickshaws, but then the Nano came along and I decided to buy one," says the long-time Mumbai resident. "After all, it was a Tata car and it cost just Rs1 lakh." Thakur, too, had fortune on his side. He made his booking on the last day for it and, in the first week of July 2009, he got a call from the dealer informing him about his allocation. "I was thrilled. I hadn't even seen the car other than on television and in the papers."

Navi Mumbai denizen Arun Kejkar, a 45-year-old accountant with an infrastructure company and another first-time car owner, also waited till the closing day for bookings to try his luck in the Nano lottery. He did not have to wait, though, for attention to come his way once he began driving the car home. "It was late evening, dark and raining, but we had a crowd of 25-30 around the car as soon as we pulled up for petrol at a pump," he says. "And then we couldn't find the petrol inlet. Everyone started searching and finally the fuel attendant thought of opening the bonnet and there it was."

Kejkar's brother had been pushing him to buy a second-hand car, but he wasn't having any of it. "I wanted a new car and I was getting the Nano for about as much as I may have had to pay for a used car," he says. The looks his car got were a bonus. "My brother has a friend who owns a car showroom near my place. When he heard I had been allotted a Nano he insisted on keeping it on display at his showroom for a couple of days, just so he could attract people." After Kejkar did get to take the car home, he got an apology from a toll plaza employee. "He said if it were up to him he would not charge me toll for passing through in my Nano."

Unlike with Vichare, Thakur and Kejkar, the Nano that Bangalore-based software engineer Bharath Brahmakal purchased was for his father. "I was the first person in Bangalore to get the car," he said in an interview. "I haven't seen any other car in the city that gets so much attention." Business manager Sumit Sukumar from Mumbai isn't so kicked about the crowd his Nano draws on the street. "It can get scary sometimes," he says. "People surround the car and ask all kinds of questions."

Chennai resident Dayanand Rao scoffed at the criticism directed at the Nano. "Ratan Tata has made it possible for lower-income groups to own a car," he said in an interview. Anil Abraham Mathew from Mumbai said it "feels good to see so many people wanting to pose for a photograph with my car" and Delhiite Kuldeep Kumar said he has become "famous thanks to the Nano". Nikhil Natani, a Jaipur student, cannot get over owning a Nano. "It seems like the whole world is watching us," he said.

Ramesh Babu is among the better-known people in Tanaku, a small town 400 km from Hyderabad, simply because he has a Nano to call his own. "The publicity I have got is overwhelming," he said. Tapan Datta from Kolkata said he would have preferred a made-in-Singur Nano, but that detracts only slightly from his joy at being one of the first people in his city to get the car. Umesh Trivedi from Hyderabad said eight members of his extended family had booked Nanos, but only he has got lucky thus far. The best compliment he has received for the car? "I was coming back from an outing with friends one night and an Audi zoomed past us, went ahead and stopped. The owner got out and waved for us to stop.

He wanted to see my Nano up close."

Cost has been, of course, an important consideration for many of those who set their heart on a Nano, but the price factor can get skewed in some circumstances. Rajesh Thukral, a suburban Mumbaite, wants a Nano. He also has to make allowance for a parking slot in his housing society that will set him back by more than what the car costs. So too Viral Shah, another Mumbaite, who said he will have to shell out Rs3.22 lakh for his Nano and a parking shelter for it.

Hyundai, Nissan-Renault, Maruti Suzuki, General Motors, the Mahindras and China's Cherry are among those looking to counter the Nano with low-cost automobiles of their own. But what about the motor car that has turned the affordability equation on its head? There has been talk of a diesel Nano, a hybrid Nano, even an electric Nano. The company is also working to craft a small car, based on the Nano, for Britain and the rest of continental Europe, the United States and Australia.

Tata Motors unveiled a variant of the Nano, dubbed Nano Europa, at the 2009 Geneva Motor Show. It has been reported that this model is superior to the standard Nano being sold in India on several counts, more powerful and luxurious, longer and wider (to meet safety regulations), with a bigger wheelbase, a new turbocharged engine, better braking systems and improved interiors and exteriors. Tata officials said at the time that the Nano Europa would go on sale in Europe by 2012, and Ratan Tata was quoted as saying there was more of the car to come. "I think the days when you designed a car for one particular region are over. There are no more borders," he said.

America is also a potentially juicy prospect for the Nano in the days ahead. "We have been looking at the United Sates," said

Ratan Tata in early 2009, adding that work was progressing on a prototype based on the Nano Europa that will meet American safety and emissions standards. The Tata Motors chairman, however, qualified his statement by saying this would have to wait until the Nano proves itself in India and then Europe. "Initially, we didn't plan to market the Nano outside India, except perhaps in some developing countries of Africa and South East Asia. We have been driven by a change in demand. We suddenly realised that it could be of considerable interest in Europe and even in the United States. It won't serve the same purpose in those countries, but will be in a niche that didn't exist before.

"A year ago, I would not have been interested in taking this car to the US. Now I think there is an opportunity for a small, low-cost, fuel-efficient car there. We are doing the design work on a version for the US right now and would like to have it in the market within three years. But there are a lot of things still to be decided. It is important that we get this right: The US is an unforgiving market."

A Tata small car for America could, it has been speculated, lead to a Nano coupe, a minivan and a convertible. "It's not out of the question," said Girish Wagh in a mid-2009 media interaction, adding that the Nano could be made "more amenable" to other versions through reengineering. Meanwhile, Tata Motors engineers have subjected the Nano Europa to front- and side-impact crash tests at the Motor Industry Research Association, or MIRA, in Britain. The tests were run under the supervision of an inspector from Britain's vehicle certification authority and in the presence of journalists from several auto magazines.

"We've conducted these tests in India, so we knew the car would pass, but it's still a great moment," said Clive Hickman, managing director of Tata Motors European Technical Centre.

What about the price at which a Nano Europa will sell? "We are trying to get the balance right between what is appropriate for a particular market and what is affordable. It's a balance between economics and the highest levels of safety we can achieve."

Ratan Tata has said he hopes Tata Motors can launch the Nano Europa in 2012 or 2013. This version will, for sure, be a lot different from its Indian sibling. Many of the features discarded during the development of the Indian model will have to be incorporated. The only confirmation from the company thus far is that the European Nanos will have a more powerful engine, a five-speed manual transmission, stability control and some luxury touches.

Developing a Nano for the developing world,

countries in Asia, Africa and Latin America, will undoubtedly prove easier. All of this can be considered as part of evolution of the idea of the Nano, as Girish Wagh, still deeply involved in the programme, points out. "The Nano as it exists is part of that evolution," he says. "The car we see today was certainly not the Nano that was envisaged. Nothing was clear, there was no benchmark, no fixed lines. We just wanted to make a low-cost car that would address a certain segment of the market. That's why we continue working on a lot of things in the current Nano. This is quite common, of course, and it is done to keep the product fresh and alive throughout its lifecycle."

Wagh believes the Nano can find space in developed as well as developing markets. "What we are currently doing is upgrading the car to meet different regulatory requirements," he says. "That means enhancing the car from the point of view of safety, emissions and performance, so we may bring in new power trains, we may bring in improvements in its suspension, and such other things." Does he think the Nano can become a global car, an icon like the Volkswagen Beetle, for instance? Wagh is less than certain. "Our first responsibility is to meet all the expectations that have been raised in the Indian market."

Beyond that, he adds, for the car to be successful across the world, it's vital that Tata Motors understand the customer and the market it expects to make a play in. "We will have to tweak the product to meet the specific requirements of different markets."

For Tata Motors and its people, the world as they knew it changed over the course of that memorable morning at the Delhi Auto Expo on January 10, 2008. Nothing has been quite the same for the organisation and everyone associated with it ever since. The Nano, for sure, has been at the heart of this makeover, but there is more to the Tata Motors story than its small car and the big bang it has made.

CHAPTER **7**

Nano in a nutshell

The Nano has come to mean many things to many people, but most of all and to most people it means a fantastic buy. Price apart, the car has a lot going for it in terms of features, creature comforts, accessories, performance and ride quality. It may seem to the outsider like a minor miracle that the engineers and others who slogged on the small-car development programme have been able to deliver at such a low cost. A closer look at the project, though, reveals innovative thinking and painstaking execution — in engineering, processes and organisationally — rather than unexplainable phenomena as the reason why the Nano is a trailblazing motor car.

Tata Motors has filed 37 patent applications and 31 design applications relating to the small-car development project. That may not seem too impressive when compared with the 200-odd patents awarded on average every year to General Motors, but patent count by itself can never be the only barometer of a company's innovation quotient. Much of the creativity that characterised the Nano project involved taking existing, patented components and technologies and rejigging them to the small car's advantage. Take, for instance, the Nano's modular design, which sets it apart in an environment where automobile design seems to have reached saturation point.

The distributed manufacturing concept that Ratan Tata, the chairman of Tata Motors, pursued for long is another example of a non-patentable idea. In this concept — currently placed in cold storage but still an option for the future — the Nano would be assembled by local entrepreneurs. Components would be built and shipped separately to be knocked together in a variety of locations. The car, in effect, would be sold in 'Nano kits', distributed, assembled and serviced by local entrepreneurs.

Speaking in an interview with the *The Times* of London in mid-2008, Ratan Tata had the distributed manufacturing concept clearly mapped out. "A bunch of entrepreneurs could establish an assembly operation and Tata Motors would train their people, would oversee their quality assurance and they would become satellite assembly operations for us," he explained. "We would produce the mass items and ship them as kits. So we would create entrepreneurs across the country who would produce the car. That is my idea of dispersing wealth. The service person would be like an insurance agent, who would be trained, have a cellphone and scooter and would be assigned to a set of customers." Ratan Tata also spoke about providing tools for local mechanics to assemble the car in existing auto shops or even in new garages in remote areas.

The idea could not be implemented right away due to concerns about quality assurance, critical in an automobile being newly introduced in the marketplace. "We told [Ratan Tata] we were not completely confident about the concept," says Santosh Bannur, a senior manager with the manufacturing planning team on the Nano project. "He was annoyed with our response, and this was one of the few occasions he showed his annoyance. He said he was sure we could pull it off from the engineering perspective, but that with everyone being less than certain, 'I don't want to force you to unwillingly do something that you are unsure will work'."

There was no doubt, however, about the pricing of the small car, set by the chairman at Rs1 lakh and accepted by the development team as the boundary they could not breach. That, of course, was easier said than done and the Nano team would struggle long and hard to keep every component inside a decided target cost. There was no option but to get innovative.

Engine: This, the heart of the Nano, is among the most expensive of the parts in the car. At 624cc and capable of delivering 35bhp, it has an engine management system (EMS) developed by the German company Bosch with fewer sensors and components than a standard unit. The EMS, a vital part in today's automobiles, is actually a computer that controls every aspect of the engine's operation. This complex piece of machinery comes at a stiff cost. The Nano team worked overtime with Bosch to drive down the price of the small car's EMS. The small car's engine combines high technology with smart packaging at a low cost. It can take the car to a top speed of 105kmph and prevent it from going any faster, and it meets all regulatory norms on emissions in India.

Engine layout: The design of the Nano's engine, which has been patented, is such that it can be placed in the rear of the car. The engine is covered in a way that is unique, giving almost no indication of its placement (other than a bit of noise when it is revved up). Located under the rear seats, it may be a bit difficult to access, but makes up for this by freeing up space inside the car, which explains why the Nano's cabin space is 21 per cent more than that of the Maruti-800. The single counter-balancer-equipped motor, as it is called, is said to be the first of its kind in the world.

Dashboard, mirror, fuel inlet and wiper: The centrally placed, bare-bones instrumentation panel in the Nano is a nifty piece of designing that saves on space and cost. The panel has a speedometer, an odometer and a digital fuel gauge, with smooth, rounded edges for safety reasons and cubby holes for storage. The Nano does not have a rear-view mirror on the passenger side of the car (this is offered as an option). The fuel filler cap is under the nose of the car and the cost factor comes into play here, too, since this does away with the need to create a hole in the side. The Nano's single-piece wiper is another cost saver.

Body: The small car's lightweight sheet-metal body delivers enormous savings in cost. With an ample crumple zone — thanks to the rear-engine setting — intrusion-resistant doors and space in front to hold a spare tyre, the Nano scores on more than one aspect. Tata Motors engineers say the car's body is stronger than that of a conventional car due to it being a combination of monocoque and the space frame that motorcycles employ. The Nano's bumpers are thinner than in other cars, its rear glass is bonded to the body for better safety, and its roof is ribbed to enhance its looks and add to the rigidity of the overall structure.

Wheels: The small car's wheels are made of a low-cost alloy, they have three lugs instead of the traditional four, and their tyres are tubeless. The Nano's wheels are small and light; this translates into superior performance and ride quality for the small car and improved manoeuvrability, not to mention lower costs. The difference in the sizes of the front and back tyres helps provide better balance to the vehicle. The small wheels and the light weight mean that the lack of a power steering will not be too noticeable.

Interiors: The plentiful space inside the Nano (for a small car, that is) has not added to its manufacturing cost. The vehicle's headrests are meshed into its lumbar support, cutting on parts required and, consequently, cost. The front seats are mounted on a rail that runs across the car horizontally, acting as a safety devise to absorb the impact of a side collision, and the cabin floor is covered with material that prevents corrosion of the underbody. The car's gear lever, cup holders and power window switches are designed to minimise assembling time. The Nano's window winding mechanism and its door-handling mechanism are both lower on cost than for any similar car.

Et cetera: The Nano's electrical fittings and electronic components are bare minimum, saving yet more on cost. The car's headlights are probably the cheapest in any mainstream automobile and its lead acid battery shares a similar costing characteristic.

Price has to be the starting point for any listing of the Nano's attributes features and specifications. The cost of the small car is, as one commentator pointed out, "roughly equivalent to the price of a DVD player in a luxury car from the West". Cost aside, there is the small matter of simplicity, and the Nano scores just as high in this regard. Much of what's taken for granted in today's 'advanced' motor cars, in terms of functionality at least, is embedded in electronics that customers know little about. The Nano is basic by comparison and that is one of its advantages.

Price and variants: There are three variants of the Nano — the standard, the CX and the LX — and their price ranges from about Rs0.12 million to Rs0.18 million. The three models differ on the following four parameters: comfort and convenience, interior, exterior, and safety and security. The standard version comes in three colours, has single-tone seats and a fold-down rear seat. The CX has six colour options, heating and air conditioning, two-tone seats, a parcel shelf, booster-assisted brakes, and a fold-down rear seat with nap rest. The LX, in addition to the features sported by the CX, has fabric seats, central locking, front power windows, body coloured exteriors in three premium colours, fog lamps, electronic trip meter, cup holder in front console, mobile charger point and a rear spoiler.

Dimensions and weight: The Nano is 3.1 metres in length, 1.5 metres in width and 1.6 metres in height. It has the smallest exterior footprint for an Indian car, with a turning radius of just 4 metres, making it manoeuvrable in the smallest of parking slots (the Maruti-800's turning radius is 4.4 metres and the Maruti Alto's is 4.6 metres). The Nano has a kerb weight of 600kg. It has a ground clearance of just over 7.1 inches and 12-inch wheels.

Performance: The Nano has a 624cc, two-cylinder, multi-point fuel-injection petrol engine that can deliver 35bhp. It is a rear-wheel drive with a four-speed manual transmission, can accelerate to 60kmph from a standing start in eight seconds and has a top speed of 105kmph. It has a fuel efficiency of 23.6 km/litre, as certified by the Automotive Research Association of India under mandated test conditions. This is the highest for any petrol-engine car in India.

Emission: At 101 gm/km, the Nano has the lowest carbon dioxide emission for cars in India. It is Bharat Stages II and III compliant and is Bharat Stage IV ready. Its high fuel efficiency rate ensures that the car has a low carbon footprint.

Safety: The Tata Nano's safety performance exceeds current regulatory requirements in India, having passed the roll-over test and offset impact. It has a reinforced passenger compartment, crumple zones and intrusion-resistant doors, besides mandatory seat belts. The car has tubeless tyres, with the ones at the rear being wider (for better balance and stability). In addition, there are safety features like collapsible steering high-mount stop lamps. The deluxe LX version has a host of other safety and security features, like front and rear fog lamps and central locking.

Other features, etc: The car has a 15-litre fuel tank and its trunk has a capacity of 154 litres. It offers customers a warranty of 18 months or 24,000km, whichever comes earlier. The car's spare tyre is under the bonnet and its battery placed below the driver's seat. The spare tyre in the Nano is the same in size as its front tyre, but this can be fitted in the rear too in case of a flat-tyre emergency (to be replaced at the nearest service station). The two scoops on either side of this car allow cool air to enter as the car moves and this helps in cooling its engine. The Nano comes in six colours: racing red, summer blue, ivory white, sunshine yellow, champagne gold and lunar silver.

Bookings: The initial phase of the bookings for the Nano ran from April 9 to April 25, 2009. The company received 206,703 applications and the Tata Nano website recorded more than 20 million hits in the fortnight following the car's launch on March 23, 2009. A booking form cost Rs300 (Rs200 for online booking) and was available at some 30,000 locations in about 1,000 cities. The forms were handed out through Tata Motors dealerships, branches of the State Bank of India and its subsidiaries and associates, other financiers, and outlets of Westside, Croma, Titan and Tata Indicom. In a first for the Indian automobile industry, the

Nano could be booked online through 34 banks. Tata Motors had agreements with 18 banks to enable customers to get finance and book the car. The company determined that the first 100,000 applicants for car deliveries would be chosen through a computerised, random selection process, and that they would receive their Nanos by the October-December quarter of 2010. On June 23, 2009, Tata Motors declared the names of the 100,000 people who had been allotted their cars, and 55,000 names of those not among the first 100,000 but who chose to retain their booking. Deliveries of the Nano began in July 2009.

Merchandise: The Nano comes with an attractive range of accessories and merchandise, including a Nano phone, a Nano watch and T-shirts. These are available online at www.tatanano.com as well at Tata Motors dealerships and outlets of Westside and Croma. Tata Indicom is marketing the Nano phone and Titan the Nano watch. The entire range of Nano merchandise is divided into categories and sub-categories to make it easy to find a particular product, and there are products for everyone from kids to adults. Among the goodies on offer are Nano caps and hats, water bottles, pencil boxes, magnets, key chains, car hangings, mobile charms, coasters, sling bags, pen sets, and pen drives and mouse pads, and apparel for men, women and children.

Accessories: There are lots of accessories for customers to spice up their Nanos. These include alloy wheels and body kits that can help with customisation. There's also an exclusive Walt Disney range of car accessories that have been designed specifically for the Nano, such as seat covers, seat-belt pads and car covers. Then there are electronic accessories like audio systems and security enhancements. Priced competitively, these accessories are available at all Tata Motors dealerships.

Marketing: Tata Motors launched an online, community-based marketing effort to generate big appeal for its small car. The Nano website features a blog and a forum which has some 20,000 members and a 'dream car configurator' that allows visitors to play with the Nano's design and create their own versions of the car. The innovative use of media to advertise the launch of the Nano won the Tata Motors campaign the 'bronze lion' at the 2009 edition of the annual advertising awards festival at Cannes. Unlike with most car launches, the Nano advertising push was not supported by a television campaign. Typical car launches have advertisement budgets of Rs200-300 million, with a large percentage of this devoted to television. The size of the Tata Nano campaign was estimated at no more than Rs50 million.

What Tata Motors has accomplished by way of its small wonder may not be as revolutionary as Richard Arkwright did in the latter half of the 18th century with his yarn-spinning machines — the rise of industry in the western world owes plenty to this idea of using machines to do at one central place what human muscle power had previously done in many — or Henry Ford, who pioneered the mass production method with his Model T. But the development of the Nano is a marker in the never-ending journey of innovation: an Indian company fashioning a new engineering template and an organisational system within the loop of solid business logic to emerge with a winner.

CHAPTER **8**

The Tata Motors story

A little over two years after the unveiling of the Nano, its incredibly low-cost car, and after its acquisition of celebrated global brands Jaguar and Land Rover, Tata Motors has catapulted itself to the world stage. Long and sometimes frustrating as this journey has been, it has paved the way for the company's recent takeoff. The Nano was a result of the vision and persistence of Tata Motors chairman Rata Tata and the doggedness of the team that designed and developed it. The decision to make big global acquisitions — including enterprises in South Korea and Spain — was part of the chairman's vision to make the company an international player; and the competencies and strength to achieve these feats have come from the way Tata Motors was built over the years.

The Nano has become such a mega event that people less familiar with the Indian automotive industry and with Tata Motors might think this trailblazing motor car is an isolated development, a one-off in an otherwise mundane story. Nothing would be farther from the truth! The Nano is a culmination of decades of effort to build engineering excellence across an extended organisation and to offer products that customers want.

In comparison with Tata Motors' slow pace of growth for over three decades, when the company was constrained by the licensing regime operating in India, what has happened in the past decade has been explosive. This is all the more remarkable because it has happened in the face of many odds, among them Tata Motors' earlier inadequate preparedness for global competition. The company has taken some hard knocks and then raised itself by the bootstraps to get where it has today. It was not the first time it did this, though.

In the mid-1980s, the relaxation of controls on the Indian automotive industry by then prime minister Rajiv Gandhi resulted in four new joint ventures being created to make small trucks (LCVs, or light commercial vehicles), each of them led by a Japanese major: Toyota, Nissan, Mitsubishi and Mazda. For many this seemed to portend the end of Tata Motors' reign at the top of the commercial vehicles business in India.

The doomsayers had not reckoned with Tata Motors' resilience, born of decades spent creating a culture of engineering expertise. Despite being a late entrant on the LCV scene (after the Japanese companies), the company quickly launched two small trucks of its own, priced competitively and with features that more than matched those of their Japanese rivals. It was clear soon enough that Tata Motors had won this battle hands down. Since then, the Japanese LCVs have more or less withered away. Incidentally, the 1980s were also the decade during which Tata Motors made a deal with Honda Motor of Japan to make the Accord in India. The proposal was shot down by the Indian government, although other proposals to make cars with foreign partners (including Suzuki and Fiat) had been previously approved. One can only imagine the frustration at Tata Motors.

At the beginning of the 1990s, around the time when the Indian government scrapped the licence raj more thoroughly and began opening up the economy, Tata Motors was in a vulnerable position. Its only business was trucks, and the trucks it made had had little infusion of technology for some time. The earlier rigid controls on industry had made this difficult, and the protection that licensing provided made it tolerable.

With licensing removed, the threat of foreign entrants with deep pockets making inroads into Tata Motors' territory loomed large; and the Indian company did not have the wherewithal to make a dent in markets outside India. The scope for growth in India was then limited as Tata Motors already had an overwhelming share of the commercial vehicles market, which is subject to the vicissitudes of business cycles. It had to break out of this trap.

When Ratan Tata suggested a way out — by manufacturing cars — many analysts got all set to write off Tata Motors. They reckoned a truck maker could not, and should not, make cars. Now, following the resounding success of the Indica and other cars, nobody questions Tata Motors' ability to compete in the car market, at least in India. The Manza, the sedan based on the Indica-Indigo platform, shows how the company has learned to offer contemporary features at competitive prices.

Tata Motors' recent successes have not been fortuitous. They have been built on the foundation of engineering talent that has been systematically nurtured over the decades, and the determination to do whatever it takes to be among the top in the global market. Even during the restrictive days before the economic reforms, the company, then led by the charismatic Sumant Moolgaokar, persisted in developing engineering talent; its internal training programmes were much admired. Those efforts continue to pay dividends.

The challenges of the past decade have been different from those of the earlier years. Since the 1990s, when the Indian market was opened wide for investment, about a dozen global automotive companies have driven into the country, and most of them launched their cars before Tata Motors could introduce the Indica, its first passenger car, in 1998. Now, Volvo has launched its trucks here, and it is only a matter of time before other global truck makers enter the attractive Indian market.

The going really got tough, and very rough, for Tata Motors at the turn of the century. In 2000-01, the company made a backbreaking loss of Rs5 billion, the biggest ever for an Indian company. Everyone was shaken up, and that perhaps was the best thing that could have happened to Tata Motors.

As the company's former managing director, Ravi Kant, who headed the commercial vehicles business when the crisis hit it, says, "We could have sunk under the weight of the loss or we could have pulled up our socks and rejuvenated ourselves. We chose to do the latter. It wasn't easy. People here were very proud, even a bit arrogant, which happens with successful organisations. The big loss dented our pride, it punched a hole in the arrogance and complacency, and a formal strategy and a business plan were chalked out for the next five years." The vision came from Ratan Tata.

The commercial vehicles market was changing dramatically, and Tata Motors had to take notice. "We had products that were good for yesterday's market, but poor for tomorrow's market," according to Kant. Many things had to be done, and done quickly. The bleeding had to be stopped by cutting costs, existing products had to be upgraded and new, international-class automobiles had to be introduced.

The people at the top, including Ravi Kant, Prakash Telang, then executive director, commercial vehicles, and currently the company's managing director for India operations, Rajiv Dube, former president, passenger cars, former executive director Praveen Kadle and chief financial officer C Ramakrishnan, contributed to the strategising and joined in the implementation of the company's ambitious plans.

Kant's role was critical at this juncture. Girish Wagh, head of the Nano development programme, recalls how Kant revitalised the organisation after he joined Tata Motors in 1999. "The loss of 2000-01 meant that morale in the organisation was low," says Wagh. "Mr Kant made us go out into the markets and meet customers; his aim was to make us more customer-focused.

"He also made people in one company location visit other locations and mix with colleagues there. Such interactions had never happened before; people had grown accustomed to working in silos. There were people who had worked for 24 years with the organisation in Pune or Jamshedpur, and had never once visited the other plant."

In order to break down the barriers dividing the organisation, Kant once organised meetings in Jamshedpur and asked people from Pune to accompany him there. "There were those who wondered why 30 employees were flying to Jamshedpur, incurring travel and hotel costs," adds Wagh. "But he had a clear objective.

Just as we could not understand what our customers wanted unless we met them, he said, we would never be able to empathise with our colleagues in other locations if we did not meet them and understand their problems."

Creating a seamless organisation that listened to the customer's voice was a goal chairman Ratan Tata had set for Tata Motors. But, although he had talked a lot about it, it did not happen in strong enough measure until Kant took the bull by the horns. He had, in a sense, no option but to try and break from the past. He began meeting young, high-potential personnel, building rapport with them over breakfast, lunch or dinner as well during the work routine. And the results started showing quickly.

After much soul-searching, brainstorming and cost cutting, every aspect of fixed, variable, interest, employee and other costs was re-examined and reworked. Tata Motors managed to reduce the breakeven point in its commercial vehicles operations from 60-65 per cent of capacity utilisation to less than 40 per cent. In two years the company made a handsome profit.

The acquisition in 2008 of Jaguar Land Rover (JLR) from Ford Motor Company brought a different kind of challenge to doors of Tata Motors. Some analysts raised a red flag about the possible adverse impact on earnings of the acquisition. They were missing the woods for the trees.

In the wake of the success of its Indica and Indigo models, no one was questioning Tata Motors' credentials to make cars. Curiously, nobody could have been more aware of — and candid about — the company's limitations than Ratan Tata. One of the things he publicly admitted, after the Indica began coming good, as Tata Motors' weakness was its limited range of cars, in comparison with the wide array of products its rivals could offer. The company has added to its product portfolio, but all these offerings would have remained in downmarket segments had it not been for the JLR buyout.

The acquisition needs to be seen not merely in terms of the prospective revenues it will generate over the years (which is, of course, important), but also from the perspective of the substantial intangible benefits it will deliver to Tata Motors, the most important of which will be the opportunity to transform itself into an advanced automotive manufacturer with global competencies. The synergies between the low-cost approach that characterises most Tata vehicles and the high-tech nature of the JLR operations could be enormous in making Tata Motors a genuinely global brand.

Look at it this way and you see no contradiction in the company trying to straddle an entire industry, from its humble small cars, including the Indica and the Nano, to the sophisticated Land Rovers and Jaguars. It is a mistake to see the strategy as one of making products for diametrically opposed market segments; what the company is doing is building the competencies to offer products in a wide section of the market.

The high-end JLR acquisition may seem glamorous on the surface, but its long-term benefits are likely to be less about glitz and allure and more about bringing in the competencies required in the upmarket segments of the automotive business. That said, the thrust of the future for Tata Motors will have to come in the mass market and in new spheres such as alternative-fuel vehicles.

In today's world, companies have to keep running to stay in the same place. To grow they have to do much more. Tata Motors is clearly not content with retaining its share in India; it is looking aggressively at world markets. Being confined to the Indian market was not what Ratan Tata had in mind when he defined a strategy for Tata Motors. His view: if you have to be competitive in India, you have to be competitive in the world. Otherwise, the Indian advantage will get eroded one day as foreign companies expand their presence on your home turf. That is how global companies think and work.

Tata Motors has exported small numbers of commercial vehicles for many years. The destinations were mainly developing countries. Breaking into the large and lucrative developed-country markets needed a different approach. It needed the acquisition of new technologies and production facilities. The breakthrough came in March 2004, when Tata Motors bought out the truck division of South Korea's troubled Daewoo Commercial Vehicle Company. This was not planned, but the opportunity presented itself and the company grabbed it with both hands.

The acquisition gave Tata Motors a large commercial vehicles operation in the developed South Korean market, with a strong potential for export. "This acquisition was a first for Tata Motors," says Kant. "Though there were many challenges, of geography, culture and language, we have been able to keep each other's identity and learn from each other. This has helped us improve our domestic market share, exports and top-line profits."

The Korean unit got much-needed financial stability and Tata Motors moved one step further on the journey to becoming a global automotive company. Says Kant: "We had been planning for some time to make trucks for the international market. But when our acquisition of the Daewoo Commercial Vehicles operations happened, we decided to build the world truck in combination with the Korean unit." Not only was Tata Motors able to develop a better truck than it would have managed on its own, it has been able to hit the market earlier.

While Tata Motors seeks technology, it brings something vital to the table: strategy and efficient manufacturing solutions. One can see the strategy in the way the company aced the small commercial vehicles business.

In the mid-2000s, the Indian commercial vehicles market was bursting with new opportunities. The government's highway and rural road expansion programmes had opened up new vistas for enterprises in more than one industry segment. The Tata Motors team studied the market, talked to customers and dealers, did some heavy brainstorming, and gained some vital insights on how the company could benefit from the growth trends in infrastructure and the overall Indian economy.

As India's road network expanded, Tata Motors realised that massive new demand would be created for smaller trucks to act as feeders plying between villages and small towns. Ten 1-tonne vehicles could split the cargo of a 10-tonne truck and carry it to 10 different destinations. Conversely, 10 such small-cargo vehicles could bring produce from villages to towns, where they could be consolidated on bigger trucks for further movement to the cities. With more roads capable of carrying motorised traffic, passenger demand for vehicles would also rise rapidly.

That is how the idea of the Ace mini-truck (price: around Rs240,000 or about $5,400) originated. The sub-1-tonne payload Ace was launched in 2005 and has become a blockbuster hit, becoming, in 2009-10, the first cargo-carrying commercial vehicle in India to sell in excess of 100,000 units (it sold 110,032). Tata Motors is expanding its capacity for this mini-truck by building a plant with the capacity to roll out 250,000-vehicles a year and it expects to export substantial numbers out of this production figure.

There's more to the growth course the company has charted for itself. Take, for instance, the market for buses, where too Tata sees significant potential for development. That's the logic that drove it to acquire Spanish bus maker Hispano Carrocera and to sign a collaboration agreement with Marcopolo of Brazil. The Tata Motors plant in Dharwad in Karnataka now makes buses in collaboration with the Brazilian company.

Perhaps the most exciting developments in the near future will centre on the Nano, which has secured Tata Motors a place in the global automotive sun. But the Nano is only one part of the expedition Tata Motors has embarked on. This is a road that will take the company even deeper into India's heartland. At the other end, it will take it across international borders and into new technologies, ventures and relationships.

Girish Wagh recalls the pride everybody in the organisation felt when Tata Motors became the first Indian company to achieve revenues of Rs100 billion (a little over $2 billion), back in 1996-97. "It was seen as a big achievement," he says, "but now we have moved well beyond that; we have grown internationally, we have acquired companies abroad. So the company has become much bigger and more complex." In the year ended March 31, 2009, Tata Motors had revenues of Rs709.38 billion, seven times the 1996-97 level.

In June 2009 Tata Motors launched its new, world-standard truck range. The year also saw Jaguar Land Rover introducing its premium range of automobiles in India and Tata Motors acquiring the remaining 79 per cent of shares in Hispano Carrocera that it didn't own. And life at the company promises to get busier still in the days ahead. The Nano's new home in Sanand near Ahmedabad in Gujarat has already started rolling out the small car and volumes will increase rapidly in a short while. Meanwhile, there are Nano programmes in place and working overtime to get the car ready for markets in Europe and the United States.

Tata Motors has now announced the development of electric and hybrid tractions. The Indica Vista electric and the Ace electric will be launched in some overseas markets by 2010. The Indica Vista electric, slated to be sold in Europe, will be the product of a joint project involving the Tata Motors European Technical Centre (TMETC) in Britain and Norwegian electric-vehicle specialist Miljo.

According to TMETC chief executive Clive Hickman, a veteran of the British car industry, the sales focus of the electric car will be Europe because the vehicle will not be suitable for India. Hickman is representative of the "internationalisation" of the Tata Motors management, as Kant puts it, and one among a clutch of seasoned hands from the global automobile industry who have been brought in to manage key areas. They include Carl-Peter Forster (managing director and group chief executive officer of Tata Motors), Ralf Speth (chief executive officer of Jaguar Land Rover) and Timothy Lerston (head of Tata Motors' advanced product engineering group).

The entry of non-Indian executives into the company's fold is part of the reinvention Tata Motors has been going through in the recent past. The Nano, on the product front, signified this in serious measure. When Ratan Tata launched the Nano as the world's lowest priced car at the Delhi Auto Expo in 2008, it changed forever the rules of the auto industry. *Time* magazine acknowledged this by including the Nano in a list of "the dozen most important cars of all time, starting from 1908 to the present", alongside legendary cars like the Ford Model T, the Volkswagen Beetle, the Chevy Belair, Toyota Corolla, the Mini and the Honda Civic.

In the two years that followed those heady days, the world suddenly seemed to have turned upside down. The global recession depressed the auto industry and the upmarket segments, which included the Jaguar Land Rover, could not escape unscathed. The Nano faced an altogether different kind of setback, caused by having to abandon its chosen manufacturing location after a huge investment and to begin assembling at temporary sites before moving to the new location in Sanand.

The good news for those at Tata Motors is that the organisation has weathered the storm, and come out stronger in the process. In the year ended March 31, 2010, Tata Motors sold 872,951 vehicles globally, 19 per cent more than in the previous year, with a 37 per cent surge in commercial vehicle sales (to 413,057 units).

In March 2010, the company's global vehicle sales rose 39 per cent from a year earlier to 101,712 vehicles, with its premium brands as well commercial vehicles registering solid growth.

The future could be far more exciting still. Having laid the foundations of a low-cost approach with the Indica, the Nano and the Ace, Tata Motors seems well placed to address the concerns of an increasingly environmentally concerned world. The company is working on hybrids and pure-electric vehicles; it is also exploring the development of hydrogen-fuelled internal combustion engines in collaboration with India's space agency ISRO (Indian Space Research Organisation).

Along the way Tata Motors has built new plants and expanded existing ones. It has launched a slew of new vehicles, among them the Indica Vista, the Indigo Manza, the Ace small truck, the Prima range of heavy trucks, a new breed of buses, the Super Milo, and the Magic Iris, a low-cost automobile for public transport. It is the Nano, though, that stands apart. It has given Tata Motors the opportunity to compete in the world market to an extent that even the Jaguar Land Rover operations cannot.

That said, there remains plenty for Tata Motors to accomplish, and concerns that need addressing before it can claim to be a truly top-quality automobile manufacturer.

"We can make improvements in a whole lot of areas," says Wagh. "For example, if we want to compete with the best in the world, we need to make our product development process significantly better. We need to take our flexibility and openness to the next level, we need to start learning more and more from benchmark organisations, and we need to improve our responsiveness to customers even further. Another area is of managing our people, giving them opportunities to develop and reveal their worth."

Soon after Tata Motors acquired Jaguar Land Rover, some of Tata Motors' India-based engineers — and Wagh was one of them — were asked to go to Britain and get a first-hand feel of some of their processes. "They were outstanding," says a thoroughly impressed Wagh. "What we saw was a mature organisation working and operating in a mature market. It was essential for them to create products within a defined frequency. The challenge for us out here is to learn from them and replicate that learning in India."

Can that be done? The answer has to be in the positive if the spirit of those driving Tata Motors forward is given its due. For those with engineering in their heart, Tata Motors is a good place to be. For the many thousands of its people who swear by the company with a fervour that outsiders may struggle to understand, there is no better company to work for.

Vivek Sahasrabuddhey, a manager on the Nano project, is one such soul. "This is a multi-product, multi-location, multi-business organisation," he says with the certainty of a true believer. "Nowhere in the world, to the best of my knowledge, will you get all these attributes under one automobile manufacturing roof."

Wagh is most passionate on the matter of Tata Motors becoming a superior organisation when he talks about what he calls operational consistency. "If you look at the best automobile companies, they are very consistent in their delivery. This is where we have a long way to go. Only when we are consistently excellent in our operations can we think of strategic interventions that can make a significant difference in the marketplace. I believe this is a tough journey and that it will take loads of conviction to make it happen."

The way Ravi Kant views it, Tata Motors has to find its own passage to fulfilment. "I don't think we should compare ourselves with Toyota or General Motors or anybody," he says. "We have our own objectives and we have our own strategy to realise those objectives. The past year or so have been for us, as a business and as an organisation, a most difficult period, but we have not wavered from our objectives, we have not cut back on improving ourselves, on improving our efficiencies."

Prakash Telang concurs with Kant while stating that Tata Motors has to make its own future if it is to realise its ambitions. "We can depend on consultants and collaborators to some extent, but we ourselves have to find the solutions that best suit us," he says. "That's how the Japanese and the Koreans did it. Go back to the good old days of the 1970s and there were all these cars that the Japanese made, very boxy in shape, very poor at corners, gaps all over and things like that. People would laugh at them, but no one laughs at a Japanese car today. The Koreans came through a similar situation about two decades later, and now we in India can perhaps do the same. And the only company from India that can accomplish this is Tata Motors."

Telang realises, though, that companies such as Tata Motors have it tougher than their Japanese and Korean counterparts did. "The marketplace is cruel. When the Japanese and the Koreans started, they were given a moratorium on their home turf. They had a protected market and they could experiment at the cost of

146 | SMALL WONDER

the Japanese or Korean users. That isn't the case in India. The Indica, for instance, had to face competition from a bunch of foreign car manufacturers when it was launched. The Indian customer already knew what a good, modern car was like. In an open market people don't care whether a car is from their country or somewhere else."

C Ramakrishnan, the chief financial officer of Tata Motors, credits the Nano with much of what Tata Motors has going for it at present. "The car has taken us to the next level; internally we have become much more confident," he says. "We are proud of what we have achieved and rightfully so. But all the attention the Nano has got us brings with it weight and responsibility, and the compulsion to continue delivering what we have done so far."

References

Chapter 1
The beginning

1. *Article in* Wired *magazine, June 2008.*
2. *Interview with Ratan Tata on www.tata.com, January 2008.*
3. *Projection by the Society of Indian Automobile Manufacturers.*
4. The Belfast Telegraph, *March 2008.*

Chapter 4
From Singur to Sanand

1. The Milwaukee Journal Sentinel, *April 17, 2010.*

Chapter 6
The world reacts

1. Mint *issue of April 10, 2010.*
2. Business Line *issue of March 19, 2010.*
3. Wired magazine *issue of June 2008.*

The Nano timeline: From vision to launch

Vision
Ratan Tata
announces his
vision of the small
car. Says ideal
price level of
an affordable
family car should
be about $2,500
or Rs1 lakh

Setting up
Tata Motors
announces that the
small car will be
produced in Singur
in West Bengal

--- **2003** --------- **2004** --------- **2005** --------- **2006** ---

Challenges
The small car
project team,
headed by
Girish Wagh,
tries out several
innovations,
different design
specifications and
engineering
changes to keep
cost levels below
Rs1 lakh

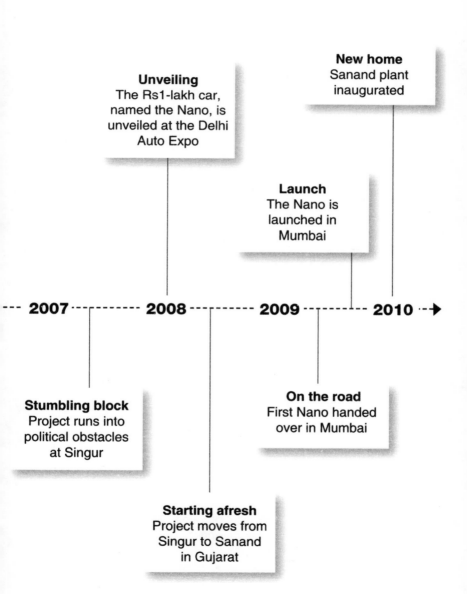

New home
Sanand plant
inaugurated

Unveiling
The Rs1-lakh car,
named the Nano, is
unveiled at the Delhi
Auto Expo

Launch
The Nano is
launched in
Mumbai

2007 ··········· **2008** ··········· **2009** ··········· **2010** ··➔

Stumbling block
Project runs into
political obstacles
at Singur

On the road
First Nano handed
over in Mumbai

Starting afresh
Project moves from
Singur to Sanand
in Gujarat